MW00634730

X.25 Made Easy

X.25 Made Easy

Nicolas M. Thorpe
and
Derek Ross

Prentice Hall

New York   London   Toronto   Sydney   Tokyo   Singapore

First published 1992 by
Prentice Hall International (UK) Ltd
Campus 400, Maylands Avenue
Hemel Hempstead
Hertfordshire, HP2 7EZ
A division of
Simon & Schuster International Group

© Prentice Hall International (UK) Ltd, 1992

All rights reserved. No part of this publication may be
reproduced, stored in a retrieval system, or transmitted,
in any form, or by any means, electronic, mechanical,
photocopying, recording or otherwise, without the prior
permission, in writing, from the publisher.
For permission within the United States of America
contact Prentice Hall Inc., Englewood Cliffs, NJ 07632

Typeset in $10^{1}/_{2}$ on $12^{1}/_{2}$ pt Palatino
by Columns Design and Production Services Ltd

Printed and bound in the United States of America

Library of Congress Cataloging-in-Publication Data

Thorpe, Nicolas M.
  X.25 made easy / Nicolas M. Thorpe and Derek Ross.
    p. cm.
  Includes index.
  ISBN 0-13-972183-5 (pbk.)
  1. Computer network protocols. 2. Packet switching
(Data transmission) I. Ross, Derek. II. Title.
TK5105.5.T48 1992   92-8709
004.6'2—dc20   CIP

British Library Cataloguing in Publication Data

A catalogue record for this book is available from
the British Library

ISBN 0-13-972183-5

1 2 3 4 5   96 95 94 93 92

In memory of our good friend and colleague
Roy Andrews

Contents

Preface and acknowledgements

The term *X.25* is probably one of the most misused and misunderstood in the computer communications industry. The biggest problem with X.25 is that it is fairly easy to pick up a few basic terms with which to impress an uninitiated audience; the use of a few key X.25 buzz-words can produce much the same effect as a magician pulling a white rabbit out of a black hat. Learning about X.25 can be an equally mysterious process. With little published material available the novice is left to either read through the CCITT (Comite Consultatif International Telephonique Telegraphique) Red Book[1] or to learn from colleagues. The fortunate few will go on training courses and come back with notes that do not necessarily relate to the real world.

We (the authors) learnt about X.25 the hard way – Nick Thorpe was involved in the design, implementation and maintenance of international packet-switched networks; Derek Ross learnt about X.25 while designing highly sophisticated military communications systems. For information we relied on training courses and the CCITT Red Book. The latter is not easy to read and is reminiscent of a legal document. We eventually ended up working together on one of the world's largest private packet-switched networks at Telerate, where we decided to pool our knowledge and write a book that would remove the mystique from X.25. The title *X.25 Made Easy* effectively summarizes our intentions, which were to make a complex subject easy to understand, using plain English and simple examples where possible.

X.25 Made Easy is not intended to be a bible, nor is it meant to be *the* definitive reference work; the latter already exists in the form of the Red Book. With *X.25 Made Easy* we have removed the mystery surrounding the subject and made a readable interpretation of the X.25 Red Book. The book should be read by those who wish to have a working knowledge of X.25 and its associated standards. Managers who need to understand the subject before taking major spending decisions should find the text invaluable. They will be provided with information that will help generate an understanding of some of the more complex data that is provided by equipment vendors. Engineers working in the field are often required to be resourceful and produce results quickly and efficiently – sometimes with a minimum of training. They will appreciate the practical nature of the book, especially Chapter 3 that deals with the physical side of X.25 and Chapter 8 that shows how X.25 is used to build sophisticated and efficient packet-switched networks. Sales personnel will benefit from the book by gaining a thorough understanding of any packet-switched equipment that uses an X.25 interface. Students will find the plain language and practical examples invaluable.

The contents

The book is structured into four main areas of interest. Chapters 1 and 2 are introductory, while Chapters 3, 4 and 5 examine the three levels of the X.25 recommendation. Chapters 6 and 7 look at more detailed aspects of the recommendation, with Chapter 8 providing a practical look at the implications of network design and use.

Chapter 1 introduces basic concepts. The evolution of packet switching is discussed and an insight given into the organizations that played a part in the formation of the standards used today.

Chapter 2 makes a specific introduction to X.25 and explains in simple terms how packet switching is used by the X.25 recommendation and how it is implemented. A closer look at the functionality of a packet switch gives the novice basic information, without which the following chapters could not be understood.

Chapter 3 addresses the X.25 physical level and takes the reader through the baffling terminology and standards that relate to cables and connectors. It is in this chapter that performance issues are first discussed.

Chapter 4 covers the rather complex subject of the frame level. This level is responsible for ensuring error-free communication. The chapter covers in detail how the protocol works, and details access procedures and sequencing.

Chapter 5 addresses the all-important packet level, that has the most significance in the interpretation of the X.25 recommendation. User data is exchanged at this level, using an environment that was set up by the previous two levels. It is at this level that addressing, bridging of networks and the procedures for setting up calls take place. It is here that readers will gain an insight into the power and efficiency of a well designed and implemented X.25 based network. The various facilities associated with X.25 (such as reverse charging), are looked at carefully in Chapter 6.

Chapter 7 covers the very large subject of PADs (packet assemblers and disassemblers). PADs were originally used to allow dumb terminals access into packet-switched networks, although nowadays a personal computer will probably have taken the place of a dumb terminal. This chapter also looks at the Triple X recommendations and their associated benefits.

Chapter 8 concerns network design, networking and associated issues such as performance, cost, maintenance and security. An example of an international packet-switched network is effectively used to demonstrate the techniques of network design.

Acknowledgements

We would both like to thank our families for their patience while we spent countless weekends and evenings working on this book. The enthusiasm and interest shown by Sally Huxtable and Robert Mauduit helped the book on its way in the early days. We would also like to acknowledge the encouragement and help provided by Colin Davies of Telerate, and to Malcolm Harris who offered assistance with some of the more detailed aspects of network design and implementation.

Nicolas M. Thorpe
Derek Ross
London
February 1992

Notes

1. The official title of the Red Book is *Recommendation X.25: Interface between data terminal equipment (DTE) and data circuit terminating equipment (DCE) for terminals operating in packet mode and connected to public data networks by dedicated circuit*, Geneva 1976 amended at Geneva 1980 and Malaga-Torremolinos 1984.

Chapter 1

Packet switching: An introduction

This chapter presents the basic concepts of packet switching, and Chapter 2 provides an introduction to X.25. These two chapters should start to remove the mystery and confusion that surround this subject. The basic concepts of packet switching are fairly easy to understand, so it is rather ironical that the expressions 'X.25' and 'packet switching' are among the most confusing and misunderstood terms in the world of computer communications.

What is packet switching?

Contrary to popular opinion, the expressions 'packet switching' and 'X.25' are not one and the same. The concept of packet switching preceded that of X.25. The term 'packet switching' refers to a sophisticated communications technology that is normally used for communications between computers and computerized equipment. It is not restricted to this activity and is gaining popularity in other areas such as the transmission of speech. For the purposes of this book we are only interested in communications between computers and computer users, i.e. 'data communications'.

With packet switching the data to be transmitted are grouped together into blocks or *packets*. Many traditional data communications techniques will transmit a long message (a page from a book, for example) from one computer to another in a continuous stream.

Figure 1.1 shows that each packet in this example contains one line of text. In practice, the size of the packet will vary in accordance with a parameter that may be altered by users to suit their particular requirements.

A packet is similar in concept to a large freight container, common throughout the world. Built to an international standard, the containers are shipped around the world with little notice being taken of their contents. Packet switching may be regarded as the containerization of computer data, and a packet can be easily transmitted from one computer to another, providing that the network it is sent on is designed to handle data in packet form.

2   *X.25 Made Easy*

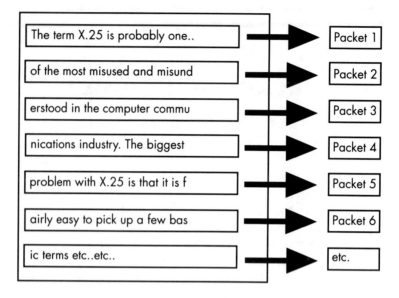

Figure 1.1   Prior to transmission, data are formed into packets of data. In this simple example each line of a page is formed into one packet.

It may be of interest to note here that the International Standards Organization (ISO) not only developed standards for freight containers, but also played an important role in the development of standards for packet-switching networks.

Communications networks

There are two main types of data communications network. One will use *packet-switching* techniques where blocks of data are transmitted between two locations. Each location may consist of computers, printers, terminals or any other type of computerized equipment. The other type of network uses *circuit-switching* technology. A classic example here is the telephone network where a caller makes a call and will have a dedicated transmission path for the duration of a call.

The main difference between these two types of network is that the packet-switched type may take any route through a network and share a common transmission path, whereas the circuit-switched user will always have a dedicated path for the duration of his call. The technique for sharing a common transmission path is called *multiplexing* and is usually the first obstacle to confuse the newcomer to the subject.

Multiplexing

One great advantage of loading data into packets is that packets from several different sources may share one common communications line. Figure 1.2 shows three terminals sending three different messages to three other terminals. This principle is known as 'time division multiplexing', a rather grandiose term that merely means the terminals share a common communications line.

Let us assume, for example, that we have three operators typing at the terminals. The operators will not be typing continuously; occasionally they will stop to look at a document or they may have tasks that do not take long to perform. These intervening rest periods allow the other terminals to use the communications circuit. This system is fine on simple networks when it is known that terminal A is always going to send data to terminal AA. When the system becomes more complex we will need some form of 'addressing' for the individual packets of data to ensure that they reach the correct destination.

The birth of packet switching

Three areas of activity fostered the use of packet switching. To begin with, 'time-sharing' companies were set up in the late 1960s to allow users to

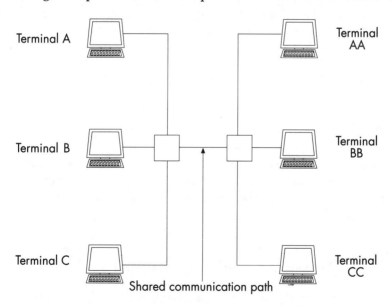

Figure 1.2 Basic concept of multiplexing: one common transmission path is shared by six terminals.

share the power and resources of large mainframe computer systems. Two of the better known networks that developed from this era are Tymshare, that became Tymnet, and General Electric Information (GE) Information Services, known as GEISCO. Tymnet is now one of the largest international packet-switching networks with over a thousand nodes on their network.

The second area of progress came with the production of dedicated communications processors by the mainframe computer manufacturers. These were designed to relieve the main computer of the bulk of communications processing. Many computer manufacturers subsequently introduced a layered structure into their communications architecture that would allow a range of devices to talk to one another. One notable example in this field was IBM's System Network Architecture (SNA) that was developed towards the end of the 1960s.[1] Other notable layered architectures were Burroughs BNA and Digital Equipment Corporation's DNA.

The rapid increase in the number of communications architectures prompted the ISO to develop some form of standards for communication architectures. The ISO proposals and their effects on packet switching will be discussed later in this chapter.[2]

Meanwhile, in the United States, the Advanced Research Projects Agency (ARPA) of the Department of Defense instigated and funded work that led to the development of a data communication network called ARPAnet. Work on this project continued from the late 1960s until the 1970s. Large mainframe computers with specific capabilities were connected together to form a network that allowed a user anywhere in the United States to access any individual computer and make full use of its particular applications.

The term *packet* was created by the ARPA research team to differentiate between the long messages that form the input into a network and the blocks that they are broken into prior to transmission across a network. This expression led in turn to the name *packet switch* being given to a particular type of communications processor.

ARPAnet used a layered architecture and the research on this project led to the development of similar networks throughout the world. Notable examples are GTE Telenet in the USA, Transpac in France and the Canadian Datapac network.[3]

International standards for packet switching

In the same way that freight containerization requires adherence to international standards, the operation of a packet-switching network will also require standardization. In this field of work the standards are referred to as 'network protocols'. A network protocol is an agreement on the format, content and management of the data being transmitted between two communications devices.

A protocol allows a standard interface to be used on several independent networks and allows computers from various manufacturers to communicate with one another. Gone are the days of computer users being tied to one manufacturer, architecture and system.

The OSI Reference Model

In 1978 the ISO formed a sub-committee to produce a set of standards that would allow computers from a variety of manufacturers to communicate with one another, so long as they adhered to a standard set of protocols. The *Reference Model of Open Systems Interconnection* (known as the *OSI Reference Model*; Figure 1.3) was finalized in 1983 and is usually known as the *seven-layer model*. It is called a model because it is presented as a good example of a layered communications architecture.

The upper four layers of the OSI Reference Model supply facilities to the user, while the lower three relate to the network. Each layer provides a common communication path to adjacent layers. The individual function of each layer is as follows:

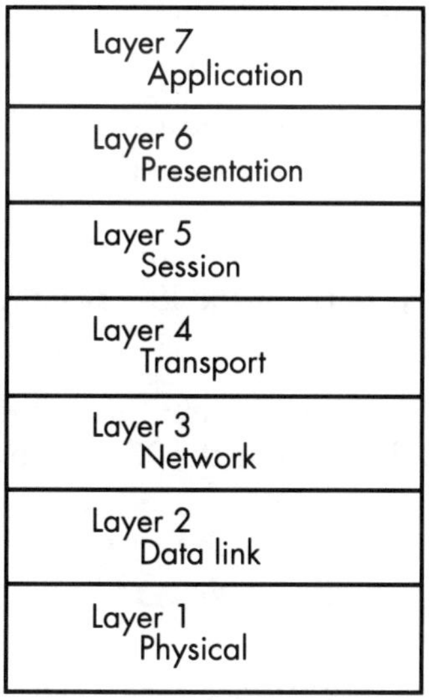

| Layer 7 Application |
| Layer 6 Presentation |
| Layer 5 Session |
| Layer 4 Transport |
| Layer 3 Network |
| Layer 2 Data link |
| Layer 1 Physical |

Figure 1.3 The OSI Reference Model.

1. Physical. The physical layer looks after the physical transfer of the
    stream of data bits that is generated by the user for transmission across
    the network. It also provides basic flow control.

2. Data link. This layer provides error-corrected blocks of data that were
    transmitted by using the error-prone physical level. These blocks of data
    are usually called *frames*.

3. Network. The network layer is responsible for routeing data through a
    network (or networks). It provides the basic multiplexing of data that
    was mentioned earlier and also looks after flow control through the
    network.

4. Transport. The transport layer provides the higher layers at each end of
    a connection with a simple transparent connection. It also provides some
    flow control.

5. Session. A session or conversation between two users will require some
    supervision during connection and disconnection. The session layer will
    look after this function and also coordinate the conversation between
    users.

6. Presentation. The presentation layer provides a form of translation
    service between the data used at the session and application layers. It
    could, for example, undertake the data formatting and code conversion
    required to convert from one character set such as EBCDIC to the IA5
    character set defined by the ISO.

7. Application. The application layer provides an interface between a user
    and the lower levels of the OSI model. It may be considered as
    providing the user with two types of service; one with programs
    provided by the user, making use of the OSI system below it, and the
    other using standardized parts of the ISO system such as electronic mail
    and file transfer.

The CCITT recommends the use of the first three layers of the ISO model for
the application and protocol layers of the X.25 recommendation/standard.

Questions

1. Who first used the term 'packet' and where was it derived from?

2. Which international organization has been responsible for generating
    standards for packet switching?

3. Name two techniques that provide network switching.

4. What is the main benefit of multiplexing?

5. Who first started to use the term 'packet' for use in data networks?

6. Give three examples of alternative layered structured communications.

7. Name the three layers of the X.25 recommendation.

8. Name all seven layers of the OSI model.

9. CCITT X.25 recommends procedures for packet-switched networks. True or false?

10. Define the term 'network protocol'.

Notes

1. 'IBM' is the registered trademark of International Business Machines.
2. M. Schwartz, *Telecommunications Networks: Protocols, modeling and analysis*, Addison-Wesley, Reading, Massachusetts, USA, 1987.
3. M. Schwartz, *Computer Communication Network Design and Analysis*, Prentice Hall, Englewood Cliffs, New Jersey, USA, 1977.

Chapter 2

Introduction to X.25

Chapter 1 provided an introduction to the basic concepts of packet switching. It was said that packet switching is effectively the containerization of computer data, and that freight containers are similar in concept to packets of data. A packet of data is merely a block of data. If a page of text is being transmitted, a packet will often contain just one line of text. A twenty-line page could therefore (in theory) be transmitted in twenty packets.

X.25 is a set of recommended procedures for accessing a packet-switched network. Before looking at X.25 we will need to take another, closer, look at packet-switched networks.

A packet-switched network is effectively any data communications system that can handle and transport data in packet form. The packets are *stored and forwarded* at each *node* along a communications path and share the temporary storage *buffers* and communications links with other packets.

A classic model of a packet-switched network is shown in Figure 2.1. In this illustration the cloud represents the packet-switched network, while the triangles are *users* and the squares are *access points* into the network. A user could be any device that is capable of handling data in packet form, such as a computer or a packet terminal.

Inside the cloud are *packet switches* through which the packets of data are routed on their way through the network. A packet switch is usually a computerized device varying in size between a microcomputer and a large mainframe computer, depending on the amount of data that is switched through the packet switch. These packet switches are known as *nodes* on the network. Irrespective of their size, each node or packet switch will have areas of memory called *buffers* where packets are temporarily stored before being transmitted to the next node in the network. It is this part of the packet switch where packets are *stored* before they are *forwarded* by the transmission part of the packet switch.

The network is shown as a cloud because a user is not usually concerned about how his or her packets of data are routed through the network. If 'A' is sending data to 'D', the packets could automatically switch through nodes

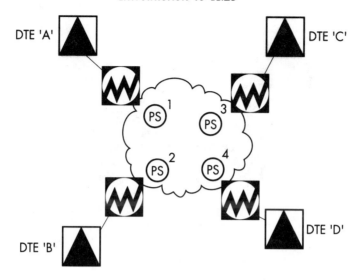

Figure 2.1 Pictorial representation of a packet-switched network. The cloud represents the packet-switched network; the triangles are *users* and the squares are *access points* into the network. The circles within the cloud are packet switches.

1–3–4, 1–2–4 or 1–4. The actual route taken would depend upon the configuration of the major links or *trunks,* and on the way that the network has been designed. For the moment we are not concerned with these connections although later on in Chapter 8 we will be taking a closer look. The path or *routeing* of packets through the network is therefore automatic and of little concern to the user.

A convenient analogy may be drawn here between this cloud model and the functions of an international container transport network. Let us assume that there is a container transport company called 'Contrans', with a network consisting of two depots in Great Britain and another two in the United States.

In Figure 2.2 there are four factories that use the Contrans network. These are owned by two companies in Britain: Smiths and Jones. Their counterparts are two factories in the United States called Kennedy and Jacobs. If Smiths wish to send a container to Jacobs they will merely load a container and send it to the nearest Contrans depot (Southampton), where it will be shipped to Jacobs using the quickest and most convenient route available. The delivery will be received by Jacobs through their nearest container depot which is in New York.

Smiths are not particularly worried about the route taken. This is left to the discretion of the network operator – Contrans. The network is therefore represented as a cloud because it is invisible to the users.

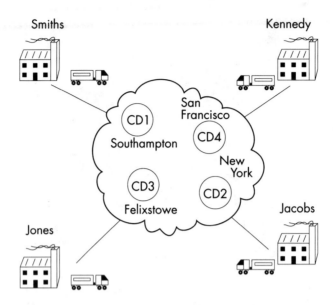

Figure 2.2   Using the containerization analogy to explain the way a packet-switching network operates.

How is a packet-switched network accessed?

Referring back to the container analogy, certain procedures will have to be followed before a container can be transported across the network. These could easily be called 'network access procedures'. It is hard to get away from standardization; the shipping and transport industry has its own set of procedures that have to be followed. Some of the information that will go with the container will be as follows:

1. Name and address of sender.
2. Name and address of destination.
3. Description of contents.
4. Type of container (chemical, liquid, dry goods).
5. List of contents.
6. Sequence number of container and total number to be sent.

Containers are normally sealed on despatch and only opened on arrival at their destination. The contents are therefore invisible to the shipper and network, although the procedural information is available for inspection at any time.

   Each user will be responsible for getting containers safely to the container depot. Once a container goes into the transport network the responsibility for it rests with the container transport company; in this case it is Contrans.

X.25: A procedure for accessing a packet-switched network

In the same way that procedures exist for the transportation of containers, there are procedures for the transmission of data through packet-switched networks. Since we have modelled this type of network as a cloud, we are only interested in access procedures. These procedures are described in an internationally agreed *recommendation* called X.25. In Figure 2.3 we have the now familiar cloud with four users attached to four network access points (remember that we are not concerned about the inner workings of the cloud as they are usually 'invisible' to a network user).

The X.25 recommendation refers to the connection of computers, computer terminals and other 'users' to packet-switched networks. It is common practice to call the user equipment *data-terminal equipment* (DTE) while access into the network is through network-terminating equipment called *data circuit-terminating equipment* (DCE). It is easy to confuse the two terms 'DTE' and 'DCE'; remember that the 'T' in DTE stands for 'terminal'. For the sake of simplicity this book will talk about 'Terminals (DTE)' and 'Exchanges (DCE)'. The term 'exchange' usefully describes the task performed by a DCE.

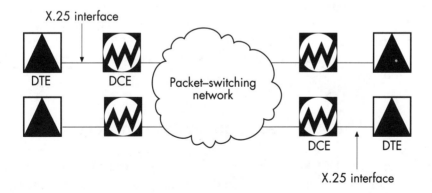

Figure 2.3 A packet-switched network will have terminals (DTEs), access points called DCEs and switches within the network.

To summarize: DCEs provide users (DTEs) with access to a packet-switching network. X.25 *recommends* the procedures that should be followed to transmit packets of data between a DTE and a DCE. Remember that X.25 is a network interface recommendation and has no jurisdiction over the inner workings of the network. Procedures for the latter are mentioned in Chapter 8.

A brief history of X.25

In Chapter 1 it was noted that there was a rapid increase in the use of computer communications networks during the 1960s. During this period it became apparent that a common protocol was required that would give users a standard interface to the new networks. Several national and international standards organizations started to look at this problem. In 1972 the CCITT (the International Telegraph and Telephone Consultative Committee) established a study group with the task of developing public data network standards. In just four years (record breaking by CCITT standards!) the CCITT had adopted recommendation X.25. This had the rather grand title of: *Interface between Data Terminal Equipment and Data Circuit Terminating Equipment for Terminals Operating in the Packet Mode on Public Data Networks.*

The year 1980 saw a revision of X.25 that became the basis of many of the X.25 implementations to date. Many national networks (such as British Telecom's Packet SwitchStream) have standardized on the 1980 revision of X.25. 1984 saw additional enhancements that sorted out some of the anomalies in the 1980 version, and provided additional benefits and facilities for users. This book has been based on the X.25 (1984) recommendation. Readers are advised to purchase a copy of the X.25 recommendation to supplement the material given in this book. The addresses needed are given in Appendix A.

The X.25 recommendation in detail

In Chapter 1 the OSI Reference Model was introduced. It is a seven-layer communications architecture around which others may be designed. Although X.25 was established before the development of the OSI model, there was considerable co-operation between the CCITT and ISO to ensure that the lower three layers of X.25 matched the equivalent layers in the OSI model (see Figure 2.4).

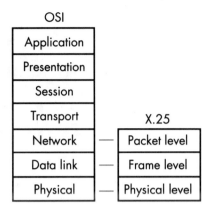

Figure 2.4   The lower three levels or layers of X.25 equate to the lower three layers of the OSI Reference Model.

If we were to look inside the packet-switched network 'cloud' we might see the situation shown in Figure 2.5, where one DTE (terminal) is communicating simultaneously with two other DTEs (terminals). These three could be anywhere in the world and the distances involved do not matter.

Virtual circuits

In the language of X.25 the two connections in Figure 2.5 are called *virtual circuits*. These form the whole basis of the X.25 recommendation as it stands today. Virtual circuits can be a confusing subject; for this reason they will be looked at in some detail.

A virtual circuit gives the user with a DTE (terminal) the impression that he or she has an exclusive and private connection with another DTE (terminal), when he or she is actually sharing communication links. By the use of clever protocols, X.25 enables up to 4096 virtual circuits to be concurrently active on any one communications link. In other words, where the term 'X.25 interface' is seen on Figure 2.5, there could be 4096 virtual circuits or simultaneous connections between a DTE (terminal) and an Exchange (DCE). In practice this number is usually much lower.

Switched and permanent virtual circuits

Virtual circuit operation is often called *switched* virtual circuit (SVC) operation to differentiate it from a similar recommendation in X.25 called

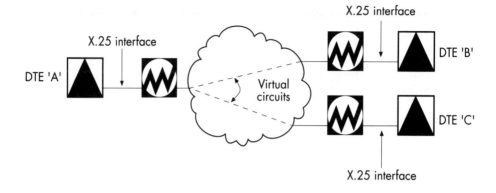

Figure 2.5 Virtual circuits: DTE (Terminal) A has virtual circuits open with DTEs (Terminals) B and C. Each X.25 interface could (in theory) support up to 4096 virtual circuits.

permanent virtual circuit (PVC) operation. With SVC operation a call is made from one DTE (Terminal) to another. After a successful connection is made, transmission of packets of data will start. When the transmission is complete the connection or call will be disconnected in an orderly manner. A PVC requires two DTEs (Terminals) to be permanently connected by a virtual circuit, ensuring that a connection is always available.

The operation of SVCs and PVCs is similar to the two types of circuit available on telephone networks, namely switched connections and leased lines. SVCs are similar to the use of an ordinary telephone where the user picks up the telephone and dials any number that he or she wishes. The connection will last for the duration of the call. PVCs are akin to leased lines where two telephones are permanently connected to one another.

The operational differences between SVCs and PVCs are quite easy to explain: PVCs are fast because there is no 'call set-up' time. (Call set-up time on telephones, for example, is the time it takes to dial the distant number and get connected.) PVCs can be expensive since the two users are permanently connected. This is particularly true if public networks are used. On a private network they will start soaking up valuable virtual circuits and place a high overhead on the network.

Datagram and Fast Select

Two other types of service were originally recommended by CCITT. These were *Datagram* and *Fast Select*. Datagram was dropped in the 1984 version of

X.25 because of a lack of interest by those companies and network providers that were implementing the X.25 recommendation. Fast Select is still available and is discussed later in this book.

With Datagram operation packets are sent into the network one at a time, complete with sufficient control and address for them to reach their final destination. Datagrams do not arrive at the other end in any particular order and will therefore require computing resources to place the packets in sequential order. It is not surprising that Datagram operation has been dropped, although it should be mentioned that the *internal* workings of many packet-switched networks use Datagram techniques. One good example here is the Canadian Datapac network that has an X.25 interface but uses Datagrams inside the network.

The three layers of the X.25 recommendation

The X.25 recommendation provides for an efficient packet mode interface into a packet-switched network. It should always be borne in mind that X.25 applies only to the interface to a packet-switched network and not to the internal workings of the network (see Figure 2.3).

A single physical communications link between the DTE (Terminal) and DCE (Exchange) allows the user to establish multiple, simultaneous virtual circuits. The control of the interface rests with the layers of the X.25 recommendation, namely: physical, frame and packet level.

Some readers may, despite previous explanations, still be confused about the functions of the layers in a layered communications architecture. For this reason we will revisit the containerization analogy that was used in Chapter 1.

The layers of a layered communications architecture work in the same way as our imaginary container transport company, 'Contrans'. Companies such as Contrans will usually be 'structured'. This term implies that each level of the organization, whether it be the President's office or the mail room, will be a vital part of the whole organization. The President sitting high up on the 31st floor of the headquarters building does not trouble himself with the day-to-day running of the company. These functions are delegated to subordinates. Various levels or layers look after different tasks that go to make the whole entity function efficiently.

The physical level

This is the lowest or most basic level of X.25. It defines the *physical* interface between a DTE (Terminal) and DCE (Exchange). The recommendations here include the voltages and signalling used, the size and type of plug and the pin connections. This level is covered in full in Chapter 3.

The frame level

The frame level's main job is to transport data across the physical link in a timely and efficient manner. The user's data are loaded into *packets* at the packet level before being passed down to this level for transmission. The packets are wrapped up with some control information and transmitted in a continuous block called a *frame*. This level in X.25 is therefore called the *frame level*, although it is often called the link level.

The packet level

This third layer corresponds to the network layer in the OSI model. The packet level primarily provides procedures for the control of virtual circuits between the DTE (Terminal) and DCE (Exchange). This sounds simple enough, but in reality the packet level procedures are quite complex and involved. The complexity is not helped by the duplication of many terms in this layer and the frame level. To avoid confusion it is suggested that readers become thoroughly familiar with the frame level procedures in Chapter 4 before moving on to the packet level in Chapter 5.

Questions

1. Define the term 'X.25'.

2. Show one way of graphically representing a packet-switched network.

3. What terms are used to distinguish between the user equipment and the network equipment? Name also the common abbreviations normally associated with them.

4. Name the international organization responsible for the X.25 standards.

5. Define the term 'virtual circuit'.

6. What is the maximum number of circuits an X.25 link can theoretically support?

7. What is the abbreviation 'SVC' short for?

8. Describe the function of each of the three X.25 layers.

Chapter 3

The physical level

The physical level is the lowest or most basic level in X.25. It defines the physical interface between a DTE (Terminal) and DCE (Exchange) (see Figure 3.1). The recommendations for the physical level include the voltages and signalling used, the size and type of plug, together with the pin connections.[1]

In many respects, this level is one of the most confusing. In the 1984 recommendation of X.25, it takes up a mere one and a half pages out of a total of 134.[2] Briefness often leads to ambiguity and this subject is no exception. The authors would note here that during our researches we were astonished by the many misconceptions and general assumptions that surround this subject. We have attempted to work through a mire of available information and come up with a *relatively* simple guide that is intended to be informative, practical and hopefully useful.

The recommendations specified within X.25 are for access to a *public data network* (i.e. a packet-switched network such as British Telecom's *PSS*), although this does not prevent the recommendations being employed on private networks.

A 'physical interface' not only provides the connection between the DTE and the DCE, but also a four part specification which can be generalized as follows:

1. Functional specifications – function of pins in a connector.
2. Procedural specification – how control is accomplished.
3. Electrical specifications – voltages, currents, speed and wave shape.
4. Mechanical specifications – type of physical connector.

The X.25 physical level or level 1 is the architectural equivalent of the physical level of the ISO's OSI Reference Model that was encountered in Chapter 1.[3] At this level, the particular requirements are defined for the functional, procedural, mechanical and electrical interface between the DTE (Terminal) and Exchange (DCE).

X.25 originally recommended the use of a classification called *X.21* for

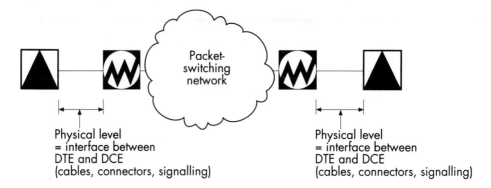

Figure 3.1   The X.25 physical level defines the physical interface between a
DTE (Terminal) and DCE (Exchange).

the physical level, together with *X.21bis* which is similar to the familiar EIA
RS–232 interface, and is intended for use on simple networks as an interim
recommendation.[4] It is important to realize that X.21 is a digital
recommendation, as opposed to X.21bis which is analogue. This was
supposed to give users time to upgrade their existing analogue communications equipment to new equipment suitable for use on digital networks. The
CCITT in 1984, under pressure from the market, made X.21bis a permanent
recommendation. This was partly because of the sheer volume of equipment
compatible with RS–232 which was already in use.

The physical level at a glance

Table 3.1 shows the various standards that are relevant under X.21 and
X.21bis. For example, at speeds less than 9600 bps[5], an RS–232-type interface
may be used with a 25-pin connector. Remember that the user is dependent
upon the interfaces offered by the network provider, and that V.28 (RS–232)
interface is the most common, especially in the United States.

X.21

In simple terms 'X.21' is the recommendation for a digital interface between
a Terminal (DTE) and an Exchange (DCE), when under *synchronous*[6]
operation on a public data network. Few public packet-switching networks
actually support X.21. It was intended to be used with the new generation of
'digital networks' that are slowly being implemented by public telegraph

Table 3.1 Choosing an X.25 physical level protocol. This table enables the
user to match transmission speeds to the relevant CCITT recommendations
from the wide range of choices available within the X.25 physical protocol.

	X.21		X.21bis			
Data rate	≤ 9600	> 9600	≤ 9600		≳ 48 K	
Electrical	X.26 (RS–423) X.27 (RS–422)	X.27 (RS–422)	V.28 (RS–232)	X.26 (RS–423)	V.35	X.27 (RS–422)
Mechanical	4903 15 pin	4903 15 pin	2110 25 pin	4902 37 pin	2593 34 pin	4902 37 pin

and telephone administrations (PTTs) around the world. At the time of
writing, the implementation of X.21 was minimal.

The recommended connector for X.21 has fifteen pins with mechanical
details and pin arrangements conforming to ISO 4903.[7] The electrical
characteristics are to be found in CCITT recommendations X.26 and X.27.
These refer in turn to the CCITT recommendations V.10 for speeds up to and
including 9600 bps, and V.11 for speeds above 9600 bps (see Figure 3.2).

X.21 signalling

Table 3.2 shows the signals provided by an X.21 interface. The following
description of the signals was taken from CCITT X.25 recommendation and
with reference to Deasington.[8]

Signal Ground

This provides a reference against which the logic states of other circuits may
be judged. Depending upon local PTT requirements it may be connected to
Protective Ground (Earth). When using shielded or screened cable the
shielding may be connected to Signal Ground, thereby reducing interference.

DTE Common Return (Ga)

This is used in unbalanced (X.26) type configurations to provide reference
ground level for the receivers within the DTE interface.

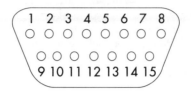

Figure 3.2   The ISO-4903 connector recommended for X.21.

Table 3.2   The circuits used in an X.25 interface.

Ref.	Circuit	Direction	
		DCE	DTE
G	Signal Ground	–	
Ga	DTE Common Return	–	
T	Transmit	←	
R	Receive		→
C	Control	←	
I	Indication		→
S	Signal Element Timing		→
B	Byte Timing		→

Transmit (T)

This is the circuit for the signals that carry data from the DTE (Terminal) to the DCE (Exchange). The data are used either in the data transfer phase or during the call set-up or clear-down phase.

Receive (R)

This is the same as for Transmit but in the direction of DCE (Exchange) to DTE (Terminal).

Control (C)

This circuit will always be 'ON' during the data transfer phase of a connection. During control phases it may be either 'ON' or 'OFF' under the control of the DTE (Terminal) to let the DCE (Exchange) know the purpose of the data on the Transmit circuit.

Indicate (I)

This allows the DCE (Exchange) to tell the DTE (Terminal) the type of data that is on the Receive circuit. Indicate will always be 'ON' during the data transfer phase, and either 'ON' or 'OFF' during call control phases.

Signal Element Timing (S)

This provides DTE (Terminal) with timing information in the form of a continuous waveform or 'clock' signal.

Byte Timing

This is used to time the transmission of each byte (eight bits) of data. This circuit will normally be 'ON' but will switch to 'OFF' at the same time that the Signal Element Timing (S) signifies the last bit of a byte.

Information on the interface is provided by the T, C, R and I signals. The normal idle or 'steady state' is 'Ready' with Control (C) set to 'ON' and Indicate (I) 'ON'. The interface will react to a sequence of states on the control signals Control and Indicate. The usual implementation has a maximum of six active interchange circuits.

The Transmit (T) and Receive (R) circuits carry user data and network control information depending on the phase of the operation. The Control (C) is used in conjunction with the Transmit (T) circuit to indicate that a call is in progress. The Indicate (I) circuit will be 'ON' when the information on the Receive (R) circuit is user data and 'OFF' to indicate that the Transmit circuit has got control information on it.

When used with X.25 both the Control and Indicate circuits should be permanently on because call control is handled by the network layer.

Timing is normally supplied by the DCE (Exchange) on the Signal Element Timing circuit. An optional Byte Timing circuit also provides a clock every eight bits to align DTE characters with the network when required.

X.21 usage

The simple example shown in Table 3.3 is reproduced from Tanenbaum[9] where the ever-faithful telephone analogy is used to explain the functions of X.21. In conjunction with Table 3.3, the following text succinctly explains the use of X.21 and is reproduced here from Tanenbaum in its entirety rather than attempt to rewrite an already sound text.[10]

Table 3.3 Example of X.21 use.

Step	C	I	Event in telephone analogy	DTE sends on T	DCE sends on R
0	OFF	OFF	No connection-line idle	T = 1	R = 1
1	ON	OFF	DTE picks up phone	T = 0	
2	ON	OFF	DCE gives dial tone		R = '+++ ... +'
3	ON	OFF	DTE dials phone number	T = address	
4	ON	OFF	Remote phone rings		R = call progress
5	ON	ON	Remote phone picked up		R = 1
6	ON	ON	Conversation	T = data	R = data
7	OFF	ON	DTE says goodbye	T = 0	
8	OFF	OFF	DCE says goodbye		R = 0
9	OFF	OFF	DCE hangs up		R = 1
10	OFF	OFF	DTE hangs up	T = 1	

Source: A. S. Tanenbaum, *Computer Networks*, Prentice Hall, Englewood Cliffs, New Jersey, 1989.

When the line is idle (i.e. no call on it), the signalling lines are all one. When referring to C and I, we will follow the CCITT practice and call one OFF and zero ON. When the DTE wishes to place a call, it sets T to 0 and C to ON, which is analogous to a person picking up the telephone receiver to place a call. When the DCE is ready to accept a call, it begins transmitting the ASCII '+' character on the R line, in effect a digital dial tone, telling the DTE that it may commence dialling. The DTE 'dials' the number by sending the remote DTE's address as a series of ASCII characters using the T line, 1 bit at a time. At this point the DCE sends what are called *call progress signals* to inform the DTE of the result of the call. The call progress signals, defined in CCITT recommendation X.96, consist of two-digit numbers, the first of which gives the general class of the result, and the second the details. The general classes include: call put through, try again (e.g. number busy), call failed and will probably fail again next time (e.g. access barred, remote DTE out of order, DTEs incompatible), short term network congestion, and long term network congestion. If the call can be put through, the DCE set I to ON to indicate that the data transfer may begin.

At this point a full-duplex digital connection has been established, and either side can send information at will. Either DTE can say 'goodbye' by setting its C line to OFF. When the remote DTE has turned off its C line, the DCE at the originating side sets R to 1. Finally, the DTE sets T to 1 as an acknowledgement, and the interface is back in the idle state, waiting for another call.

The procedure for incoming calls is analogous to that for outgoing calls. If an incoming call and outgoing call take place simultaneously, known as a *call collision*, the incoming call is cancelled and the outgoing call is put through. CCITT made this decision because it may be too late at this point for some DTEs to re-allocate resources already committed to the outgoing call.

X.21bis

The term 'bis' in X.21bis means 'twice' or 'the second'. X.21bis could easily have been called X.21 Version 2 or Revision 2. The CCITT only intended X.21bis to be used for an 'interim' period to allow time for existing equipment to be upgraded to meet the specification of X.21. Under market pressure the CCITT eventually agreed in 1984 to keep X.21bis as a permanent recommendation. The main reason for this was the proliferation of V-series interface equipment that was already connected to the networks. At the time of writing, X.21bis was the most widely used recommendation.

X.21bis allows a choice from four different leased circuit interfaces on a public data network. As may be seen from Table 3.1, at speeds up to and including 9600 bps one can either use V.28 (RS-232) or X.26 (RS-423), together with the common DB25 ISO-2110 connector shown in Figure 3.3. At 48 kbps there is a choice between V.35 and X.27 (RS-422), together with an ISO-2593 (34-pin) connector (Figure 3.4).

RS-232

RS-232-C is the third revision of the original RS-232 standard. It was formulated by a US association of manufacturers from the electronics industry, the Electronic Industries Association (EIA). RS-232 should correctly be called EIA RS-232-C. Remember that this is only a standard for the United States. The international standard is given in CCITT recommendation *V.24* which is similar to RS-232-C apart from slight differences in some infrequently used circuits.[11]

RS-232-C is suitable for synchronous and asynchronous communications along with all classes of service whether they be dedicated, leased, point-to-point, multipoint, two or four wire services and switched networks.[12]

Mechanically, RS-232-C calls for the well known ISO-2110, 25-pin, 'D'-type connector (see Figure 3.3). Electrically, RS-232 is unbalanced (i.e. all interface signals share a common electrical ground). Any voltage more negative than −3 volts is deemed to be a binary 1 (mark), and a voltage more positive than +3 volts is a binary 0 (space). See Figure 3.5.

Speeds up to 9600 bps are permissible and cable lengths may be up to 15 metres. These two factors of speed and cable length are the worst restrictions of RS-232-C and it is for this reason that the RS-449 standard was developed. RS-449 will be discussed below.

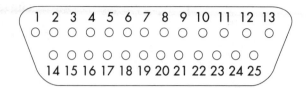

IS 2110–25-PIN

Figure 3.3   The familiar ISO-2110 25-pin connector recommended for use with EIA RS–232.

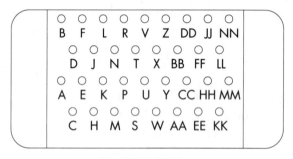

IS 2593-34-PIN

Figure 3.4   ISO-2593 34-pin connector for use with X.21 at transmission speeds of 48 kbps.

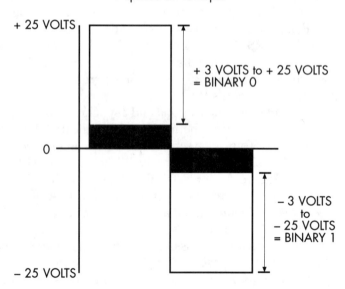

Figure 3.5   Electrical characteristics of RS–232.

Twenty interchange circuits including ground are defined in RS–232–C although only nine are usually used. The signals are divided into four groups, namely Data, Control, Timing and Ground. Table 3.4 shows the twenty interchange circuits that are specified in RS–232–C and Figure 3.6 shows the nine that are usually used.[13]

RS–449

RS–232 has been around for years and is a very popular and widely used interface standard. It always suffered from two shortcomings that eventually became intolerable. These were the inability to work reliably above 20 kbps and the limitation of 15 metres on cable length. The EIA acknowledged the

Table 3.4 The twenty-five RS–232 interchange circuits.

	PIN	Code	CCITT equiv.	Circuit	To DTE	To DCE
Ground	1	AA	101	Protective Ground		
	7	AB	102	Signal Ground		
Data	2	BA	103	Transmitted Data		→
	3	BB	104	Received Data	←	
Control	4	CA	105	Request to Send		→
	5	CB	106	Clear to Send	←	
	6	CC	107	Data Set Ready	←	
	20	CD	108.2	Data Terminal Ready		→
	22	CE	125	Ring Indicator	←	
	8	CF	109	Line Detector*	←	
	21	CG	110	Signal Quality Detector	←	
	23	CH	111	DTE Rate		→
	18	CI	112	DCE Rate	←	
Timing	24	DA	113	DTE Timing		→
	15	DB	114	DCE Timing	←	
	17	DD	115	Received Timing	←	
	14	SBA	118	Secondary Transmitted Data		→
	16	SBB	119	Secondary Received Data	←	
	19	SCA	120	Secondary Request to Send		→
	13	SCB	121	Secondary Clear to Send	←	
	12	SCF	122	Secondary Line Detector	←	

* Often called *Carrier Detect*.

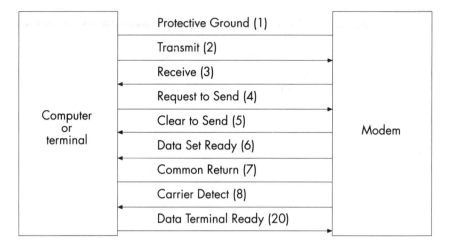

Figure 3.6   The nine interchange circuits that are usually used.

need to move forward and make technical progress. They debated for a long time about either using a totally new and technically innovative standard that was unfortunately incompatible with RS–232–C, or finding a new standard that would remain compatible with the old one. Like all good and democratic bodies they eventually came up with a compromise.

The new standard *RS–449* rolls three standards into one. The mechanical, functional and procedural interfaces are stated in RS–449, while the electrical standard is given in two other standards, namely *RS–423–A* and *RS–422–A*.

RS–423–A is similar to RS–232–C in that it uses *unbalanced transmission* (i.e. all circuits share a common ground). For this reason RS–423 is only suitable for transmission speeds up to 20 kbps. RS–422–A uses *balanced transmission* (i.e. each of the main circuits require two wires with no common ground). This allows RS–422–A to operate at speeds up to 20 Mbps (20 million bits per second) at distances in excess of 60 metres. Higher speeds are obtainable if this distance is reduced.

Figure 3.7 shows the ISO-4902 connectors for RS–449. Table 3.5 shows a comparison between the interchange circuits of RS–232–C, V.24 and RS–449. Because of the inclusion of extra circuits, the familiar ISO-211 25-pin connector was dropped in favour of the 37-pin ISO-4902 connector. The 9-pin connector is only required if the second (reverse) channel is being used.

Using the electrical characteristics of both RS–422 and RS–423, RS–449 divides the interchange circuits into two groups called categories. Category 1 includes the following ten circuits:

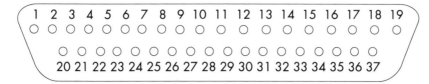

IS 4902–37-PIN

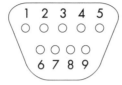

IS 4902–9-PIN

Figure 3.7 ISO-4902 connectors for use with RS–449. The 9-pin connector is only required if the second (reverse) channel is in use.

1. Send Data.
2. Receive Data.
3. Terminal Timing.
4. Send Timing.
5. Receive Timing.
6. Request to Send.
7. Clear to Send.
8. Receiver Ready.
9. Terminal Ready.
10. Data Mode.

Category 1 circuits can use either balanced (RS–422) or unbalanced (RS–423) generators below transmission rates of 20 kbps. Above 20 kbps they must used balanced generators. Any interchange circuits not found in category 1 are deemed to be category 2. Category 2 circuits use the unbalanced characteristics of RS–423 for all applications regardless of data rate.

As with RS–232, RS–449 defines thirty functional interface circuits. Once again these are divided into four groups or classifications, i.e. Data, Control, Timing and Ground. Ten of these are new, and are therefore not covered by the RS–232 specification.

The ten new circuits in RS–449 are as follows:

1. *Send Common* (SC) is connected to the DTE circuit ground as a DCE reference for unbalanced receivers.
2. *Receive Common* (RC) is connected to the DCE circuit ground as a DTE reference for unbalanced receivers.

Table 3.5 Comparison between RS-232-C, V.24 and RS-449.

RS-232-C			CCITT V.24			RS-449		
Code	Pin	Circuit	Code	Pin	Circuit	Code	Pin	Circuit
AA	1	Protective Ground	101	1	Protective Ground	–	1	
AB	7	Signal Ground	102	7	Signal Ground	SG	19	Signal Ground
						SC	37	Send Common
						RC	20	Receive Common
BA	2	Transmitted Data	103	2	Transmitted Data	SD	4,22	Send Data
BB	3	Received Data	104	3	Received Data	RD	6,24	Receive Data
CA	4	Request to Send	105	4	Request to Send	RS	7,25	Request to Send
CB	5	Clear to Send	106	5	Ready for Sending	CS	9,27	Clear to Send
CC	6	Data Set Ready	107	6	Data Set Ready	DM	11,29	Data Mode
CD	20	Data Terminal Ready	108	20	Data Terminal Ready	TR	12,30	Terminal Ready
CE	22	Ring Indicator	125	22	Calling Indicator	IC	15	Incoming Call
CF	8	Line Detector	109	8	Line Detector	RR	13,31	Receiver Ready
CG	21	Signal Quality	110	21	Signal Quality	SQ	33	Signal Quality
CH	23	DTE Rate	111	23	DTE Rate	SR	16	Signalling Rate
CI	18	DCE Rate	112	18	DCE Rate	SI	2	Signalling Indicators

						IS	28	Terminal in Service
			136	11	New Signal	NS	34	New Signal
			126		Select Frequency	SF	16	Select Frequency
DA	24	DTE Timing	113	24	DTE Timing	TT	17,35	Terminal Timing
DB	15	DCE Timing	114	15	DCE Timing	ST	5,23	Send Timing
DD	17	Receiver Timing	115	17	Receiver Timing	RT	8,26	Receive Timing
SBA	14	Transmitted Data	118	14	Transmitted Data	SSD	3	Send Data
SBB	16	Received Data	119	16	Received Data	SRD	4	Receive Data
SCA	19	Request to Send	120	19	Line Signal	SRS	7	Request to Send
SCB	13	Clear to Send	121	13	Channel Ready	SCS	8	Clear to Send
SCF	12	Line Detector	122	12	Line Detector	SRR	2	Receiver Ready
						LL	10	Local Loopback
						RL	14	Remote Loopback
						TM	18	Test Mode
						SS	32	Select Standby
						SB	36	Standby Indicator

Source: EIA Standard RS–449, Electronic Industries Association.

3. *Terminal in Service* (TS) indicates whether the DTE is available.
4. *New Signal* (NS) is intended for use in multipoint polling systems[14] where a number of remote stations will respond in rapid succession. NS tells the DCE to prepare for this condition by adjusting timing recovery and synchronization circuits.
5. *Select Frequency* (SF) selects the transmit and receive frequency bands of a DCE.
6. *Local Loopback* (LL) allows the DTE to loop the transmit analogue side of the local modem to the receive side for testing purposes.
7. *Remote Loopback* (RL) allows a DTE to loop the digital side of a remote modem, usually for testing purposes.
8. *Test Mode* (TM) indicates that the DCE is in a test condition, e.g. local or remote loopback.
9. *Select Standby* (SS) selects back-up communication channels when available and needed.
10. *Standby Indicator* (SI) DCE indicating that it is conditioned to operate in the standby mode.

EIA–RS–422 (Compatible with X.27 and V.11)

The EIA RS–422 electrical interface was designed to give considerably better performance than RS–232–C, while retaining compatibility with RS–232–C. RS–423 was originally intended to be the next generation of electrical interface standards. RS–422 is fully compatible with its CCITT counterparts X.27 and V.11.

RS–422 uses *balanced transmission* (i.e. each circuit has two wires without a common ground). A balanced circuit is much less susceptible to electrical 'noise'. It offers advantages such as longer cable distances and higher data transmission rates. RS–422 will operate with twisted pair telephone cable at 100 kbps up to 1200 metres. Data rates up to 10 Mbps are achievable at short distances up to 12 metres. These characteristics make it possible to connect equipment within a building without the need for expensive communications equipment. An optional cable termination with a 100 ohm load may be used to increase the overall speed of transmission at the expense of the maximum viable cable length.

The signalling levels of RS–422 are particularly suited to the ±5 volt levels that are supplied by most computer power supplies; these are the working voltages for many computer components, such as integrated circuits. The signalling for RS–422 is shown in Figure 3.8.

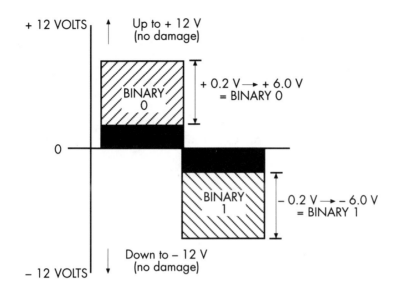

Figure 3.8 Signalling for RS–422. The signal may range between ±12 V without causing damage. Binary '0' is represented by +0.2 to +6 V, and binary '1' by –0.2 to –12 V.

EIA–RS–423 (compatible with V.10 and X.26)

RS–423 is an EIA electrical interface standard designed to provide improved performance over RS–232. It is part of the RS–449 family which also includes RS–422. The CCITT equivalents of RS–423 are X.26 and its telephone counterpart V.10. RS–423 and X.26/V.10 are fully compatible.

RS–423 is an unbalanced electrical interface but operates with a balanced receiver. Two common returns are used, one for each direction. These are grounded at the generator end. The improved design of RS–423 significantly improves its performance in terms of noise generation and susceptibility.

The complete unbalanced voltage, digital interface consists of a low impedance generator, an interconnecting cable and a high impedance differential receiver. The generator and receiver characteristics are specified in RS–423 (V.26) in terms of direct electrical measurements. Interconnecting cable requirements are given in terms of both electrical and physical characteristics.

RS–423 can operate over 24-gauge twisted pair cable at distances up to 1200 metres with transmission speeds of up to 1200 bps. Speeds up to

60 kbps can be achieved at 17 metres. The maximum transmission speed with this interface is about 300 kbps.

The signalling for RS–423 is the same as for RS–232 (see Figure 3.5).

CCITT V.35

V.35 is the CCITT recommendation for data transmission at a speed of 48 kbps. The electrical characteristics of the interface are extensively used for high speed DTE to DCE interfaces.

The V.35 electrical characteristics are a combination of an unbalanced voltage and a balanced current mode. Data and clock circuits are driven by balanced generators. These are not compatible with RS–422 circuits. Control signals are unbalanced and compatible with RS–232.

V.35 uses a 34-pin connector specified in ISO 2593 (see Table 3.6). The function of the interchange circuits is identical to RS–232.

Questions

1. Describe the function of the physical layer.

2. What is the difference between X.21 and X.21bis?

3. Note the main differences between RS–422 and RS–423.

Table 3.6 V.35 interchange circuits.

Pin	Function	RS–232 equivalent	CCITT equivalent
A	Protective Ground	AA	101
B	Signal Ground	AB	102
C	Request to Send	CA	105
D	Clear to Send	CB	106
E	Data Set Ready	CC	107
F	RCV Signal Detect.	CF	109
R, T	Receive Data	BB	104
V, X	Receive Clock	DD	115
P, S	Transmit Data	BA	103
Y, a	Transmit Clock	DB	114
m	Reserved for Test	–	–

4. Pin 7 on an RS–232-type interface is 'Signal Ground'. True or false?

5. The abbreviation 'bps' is short for 'bytes per second'. True or false?

6. What is the function of the C and I signals on an X.21 interface?

7. What would be the maximum permissible length of cable for an RS–232 interface operating at 20 000 bps?

8. Name the four groups used to define the interchange circuits for RS–232.

9. Explain the difference between 'balanced' and 'unbalanced' and name an interface standard that uses both.

Notes

1. Additional information on this complex subject may be found on pp. 52–115 of A. S. Tanenbaum, *Computer Networks*, Prentice Hall, Englewood Cliffs, New Jersey, USA, 1989.
2. CCITT Recommendation X.25, 1984.
3. See Chapter 1, p. 5.
4. 'EIA' is the abbreviation for the Electronic Industries Association – a US organization.
5. The abbreviation 'bps' is short for 'bits per second' which equates to the speed of data transmission.
6. See the Glossary for explanation of this and other terms.
7. International Standards Organization (Standard ISO 4903).
8. Reproduced with permission from R. J. Deasington, *X.25 Explained*, Ellis Horwood, London, UK, 1985.
9. p. 83 in A. S. Tanenbaum, *Computer Networks*, Prentice Hall, Englewood Cliffs, New Jersey, USA, 1989.
10. Reproduced from pp. 83–4 of A. S. Tanenbaum, *Computer Networks*, Prentice Hall, Englewood Cliffs, New Jersey, USA, 1989.
11. See *RS–232 Made Easy* by Martin D. Seyer, Prentice Hall, Englewood Cliffs, New Jersey, USA, 1984, for an excellent guide to this potentially confusing subject.
12. See the Glossary for explanation of these and other terms.
13. Readers are reminded to see *RS–232 Made Easy* for a simple and thorough explanation of RS–232.
14. See the Glossary for an explanation of this and other technical terms.

Chapter 4

The frame level

The X.25 frame level is the second of the three levels that together make up the X.25 recommendation. You may remember from the introduction to X.25 in Chapter 2 that the three levels of X.25 relate to the three lower layers of the OSI Reference Model.

Functions of the frame level

The X25 frame level has four distinct functions:

1. It provides an efficient means of transferring data across the link.
2. It keeps the Terminal (DTE) and Exchange (DCE) in step with one another, i.e. it synchronizes the link.
3. It checks for errors and attempts to recover them.
4. It gives the packet level up-to-date reports on the status of the link.

From the above we can see that the frame level's main job is to transport data across the link in a timely and efficient manner. A user's data are loaded into *packets* at the packet level before being passed down to this level for transmission. The packets are wrapped up with some control information and transmitted in a continuous block called a *frame*. This level in X.25 is therefore called the *frame level*; occasionally it is called the link level, although we will use the expression 'frame level'.

The actual framing is looked after by a bit-oriented protocol, specified by the CCITT and called *high level data link control* (HDLC). An optional character based procedure called 'Bisync' (binary synchronous) will occasionally be encountered. It is not supported on many networks and has been superseded by HDLC; consequently a description of Bisync framing has not been included in this book.

High level data link control (HDLC)

In Figure 4.1 we see that an HDLC frame consists of six components.

The flag

All frames have *flags* to mark the beginning and end of a frame. A flag is always a fixed pattern of eight bits (01111110). Note that a group of eight bits is usually called an *octet* (Figure 4.2).

If several frames are being transmitted consecutively, the end flag of one frame may be used as the start flag of another frame (Figure 4.3). It is worth noting here that flags are continuously transmitted by both the Terminal (DTE) and the Exchange (DCE) when frames are not being transmitted. This synchronizes communications between the two devices.

Transparency

It is quite possible that there could be information to be loaded into a frame that has the same bit pattern as a flag (i.e. 01111110). If this was transmitted a *false flag* would be detected by the receiver. A technique called *transparency*

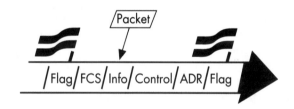

Figure 4.1   Fields in an HDLC frame (right to left): Flag, Address, Control, Information, Frame Check Sequence, Flag.

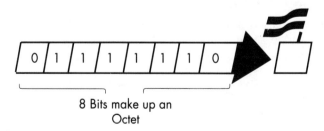

Figure 4.2   A flag in an HDLC frame is a fixed pattern of eight bits: [01111110].

Figure 4.3   When several frames are being transmitted consecutively, the end
flag of one frame may be used as the start flag of another frame.

is used to overcome this problem: after a start flag has been sent, the
transmitter will insert a zero (0) bit whenever it encounters five one (1) bits
that are not part of a flag. The added zeros will be removed by the receiver.

Aborting a frame

If the transmitter is sending a frame and decides to abort, it will transmit
seven or more consecutive '1' bits. When this code is received the receiver
will reject any data that have been received for the current frame and wait
for the next valid frame.

The address field

It is easy to confuse the term 'address' used here with the network user
address (NUA) found in the X.25 packet level. The functions of these two
'addresses' are quite different.

HDLC is a full duplex protocol that allows commands and responses to
be sent simultaneously by both the Terminal (DTE) and the Exchange (DCE).
The HDLC address field indicates which device has generated the frame and
whether it contains a command or a response to a command.

The address field will only ever have two values:

1.   00000011 called 'Address A'.
2.   00000001 called 'Address B'.

A frame containing a command and originating from the Exchange (DCE)
will have the address field set to Address A. A frame from the DTE
containing a response to this command will also have its address field set to
'A' (Figure 4.4).

The frame check sequence (FCS)

The frame check sequence (FCS) contains a 16-bit sequence that is used to
check for transmission errors across the link. The transmitter will generate

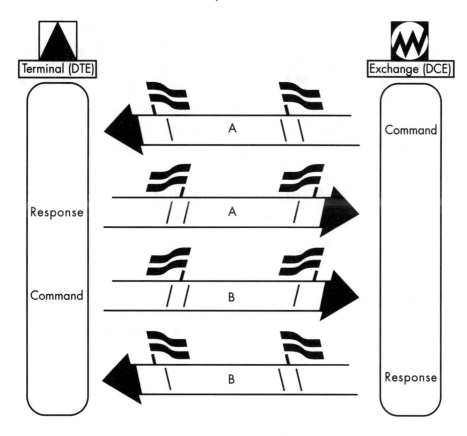

Figure 4.4 Address fields are used to identify the origin of a command. 'A' (from the DCE) is the binary pattern 00000011, and 'B' (from the DTE) is 00000001.

an FCS for all the bits in a frame between the final bit of the start flag and the first bit of the FCS sequence. The receiver will check the incoming data, including the FCS field. If the check is incorrect the frame will be deemed corrupt and will be promptly discarded.

The control field

The control field contains eight bits and is more complex than the other frame components. It indicates the type of frame that is being transmitted.

There are three types of frame; one will have an information field, and the other two perform administrative functions:

1. Information frames (I-frames): these are used for the transfer of packet information. They may also contain data for frame level flow control.
2. Supervisory frames (S-frames): the supervision of the link is handled by these frames. One function, for example, is to acknowledge receipt of I-frames.
3. Unnumbered frames (U-frames): unnumbered frames provide additional link control functions and are used during the setting up and clearing of the link.

Control field format

The P/F bit

The P/F (poll/final) bit is used to request an immediate response to a frame that has been transmitted. When a frame is sent with the poll bit set to 1, the remote end will immediately reply with a frame that has its final bit set to 1. The P/F bit is therefore a poll bit when issued as a command, and a final bit when issued as a response.

Frame numbering and frame variables

Some method is required to number some of the frames that are transmitted across the link. These sequence numbers are called the 'frame variables'.

Each information frame is given a sequence number ranging from 0 to 7. The variables that keep track of these numbers are maintained by the 'frame handler'. The concept is fairly straightforward, although it looks more complicated than it actually is.

In simple terms, a variable V(S), [V-SEND] is the sequence number that will be attached by the Terminal (DTE) or Exchange (DCE) to the next information frame to be transmitted (Figure 4.5).

V(R) [V-RECEIVE] is the next frame number that the Terminal (DTE) or Exchange (DCE) expects to receive. The location of the sequence numbers is shown in Figure 4.6.

As an example (see Figure 4.7) assume that V(S) and V(R) on both the Terminal (DTE) and Exchange (DCE) have been reset to zero (0). The Terminal (DTE) sends a frame with N(S)=0 and increments its own V(S) to 1. The Exchange (DCE) is expecting to receive frame (0), matching the value of its own V(R) of (0).

If the Exchange (DCE) is happy with the frame it will accept it and

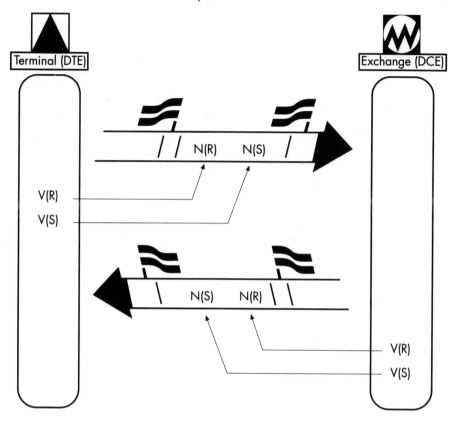

Figure 4.5   Frames transmitted across the link are given sequence numbers called 'frame variables'.

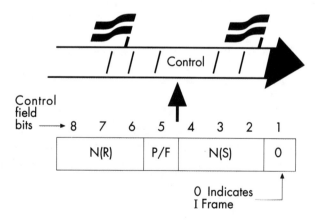

Figure 4.6   Location of frame variables within control field.

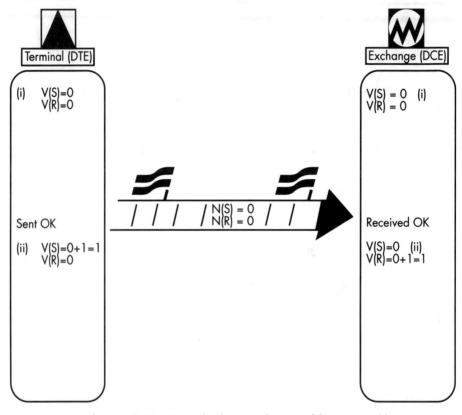

Figure 4.7   Example showing the use of frame variables.

increment its V(R) to 1. If the Exchange (DCE) did not like the frame it could scrap it and send a rejection (REJ) to the DTE, quoting the sequence number as a reference.

Remember that this numbering system works in both directions.

Information frames

Information frames will contain either control information or a 'packet' of data that has been generated by an end user (Figure 4.8). It is important to remember that the data held in a packet are transparent to the frame level interface.

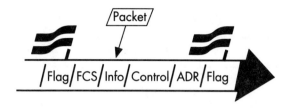

Figure 4.8 Information frames will either contain control information or a 'packet' of data that has been generated by an end user.

Supervisory frames

These frames supervise the operation of the link. Notice how they do not have an information (I) field.

There are three types of S-frames associated with the coding of an S-frame's control field:

1. Receiver Ready   (RR).
2. Reject   (REJ).
3. Receiver Not Ready   (RNR).

Note that these frame types bear no relation to the three packet types that have identical names.

In Figure 4.9 bits 1 to 4 indicate the function of the supervisory frame.

Receiver Ready response

(RR) frames may be used for the following:

1. To indicate that the receiving device is ready to receive another I-frame.
2. To acknowledge receipt of I-frames numbered up to $N(R) - 1$.
3. To clear a busy condition.

Reject response

The REJ response is used to request retransmission of I-frames starting with the frame numbered $N(R)$. The REJ frame will also acknowledge receipt of I-frames numbered from $N(R) -1$ and below.

It should be noted that only one REJ condition can exist for a given direction of data transfer and the REJ condition will only be cleared upon receipt of an I-frame that has an $N(S)$ equivalent to the $N(R)$ of the REJ response.

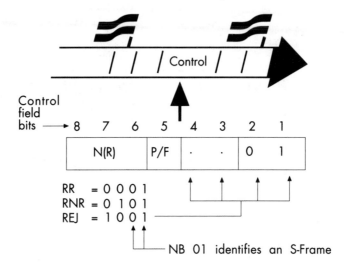

Figure 4.9 Supervisory frames (S-frames) are located in the control field; these frames supervise the operation of the link.

Receiver Not Ready response

RNR is basically used by either the DTE or Exchange (DCE) to indicate that it is busy and therefore unable to receive any more I-frames. The (RNR) response can acknowledge receipt of I-frames numbered up to and including $N(R) - 1$.

The busy condition may be cleared by the busy device transmitting a (UA), (RR), (REJ) or (SABM) command. A (DISC) or (DM) frame will clear the busy condition but will also bring down the link. (See below for a description of these commands and responses.)

Unnumbered frames

Unnumbered frames are used during link set-up, disconnect and reset (Figure 4.10). It is not really possible to look at unnumbered frames without examining the procedures that manage the link.

LAPB and LAP

The CCITT-recommended procedures for controlling the link are called 'link access procedures balanced' (LAPB). LAPB allows the link to be initialized with just one command, whereas with the earlier 'link access procedures'

Control field bits

	8	7	6	5	4	3	2	1	
Set async. balanced mode	0	0	1	P	1	1	1	1	SABM
Disconnect	0	1	0	P	0	0	1	1	DISC
Unnumbered Acknowledgement	0	1	1	F	0	0	1	1	UA
Disconnected mode	0	0	0	F	1	1	1	1	DM
Frame Reject	1	0	0	F	0	1	1	1	FRMR

Figure 4.10 The five unnumbered frames are used during link set up, disconnect and reset.

(LAP), link initializing commands had to be issued by both the DTE (Terminal) and the Exchange (DCE).

LAPB procedures

The LAPB procedures will be looked at initially and then the minor differences noted between LAPB and LAP.

LAPB commands

Set Asynchronous Balanced Mode (SABM)
This command is primarily used to set the link up in both directions. Upon receipt of a SABM command the receiving DTE or Exchange (DCE) will send an Unnumbered Acknowledgement (UA) response.

Disconnect (DISC)
Used to initiate the disconnection of the link, it will be acknowledged by a (UA) response.

LAPB responses

Unnumbered Acknowledgement (UA)
A (UA) will acknowledge receipt of unnumbered frames.

Frame Reject (FRMR)
This unnumbered frame is used to report an error condition that is not recoverable by the retransmission of an identical frame. An information field

containing twenty-four bits (three octets) gives the reason for the FRMR being generated (Figure 4.11).

V(S) and V(R) are respectively the current send state variable and receive state variable of the device that is rejecting the frame.

The differences between LAP and LAPB

These are the differences between LAPB and LAP:

1. With LAP the S-frames are only responses, not commands.
2. Set Asynchronous Response Mode (SARM) establishes the link in each direction.
3. The Command Reject (CMDR) indicates an error condition that cannot be overcome by retransmitting an identical frame.

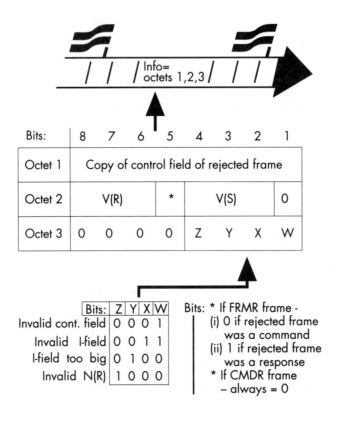

Figure 4.11   An information field containing twenty-four bits (three octets) gives the reason for a frame being rejected.

Link down state for LAPB and LAP

This is the condition of the link when the physical level either has failed or is being brought up for the first time. The Exchange (DCE) will typically send (DISC) commands to the DTE at an interval generated by Timer (T1); this timer will be looked at later in this chapter (Figure 4.12).

Setting up the link (LAPB)

The link between the Terminal (DTE) and Exchange (DCE) will have to be initialized before any data can be transmitted across it. We will assume here that level 1, the 'physical level', is operating satisfactorily, and that the

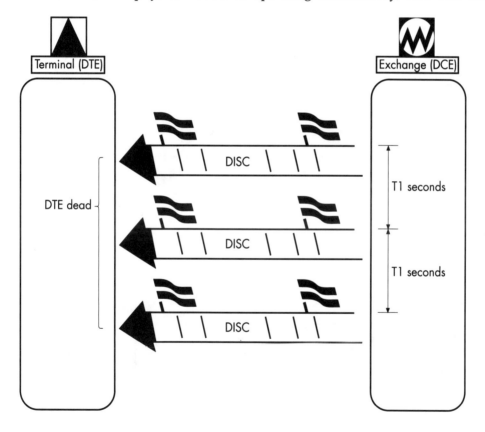

Figure 4.12 Link down state for LAPB and LAP. The Exchange (DCE) will usually send (DISC) commands to the DTE (Terminal) at intervals determined by Timer (T1).

Exchange (DCE) is transmitting (DISC) commands as shown in Figure 4.12.

In Figure 4.13 we see that under LAPB just one command (SABM) will establish the link while LAP needs four. The link set-up command for LAPB is SABM, LAP uses SARM. Remember: SABM for LAPB.

Information transfer

By this stage the link should be initialized and ready to start transmitting information frames. For the sake of simplicity, the example in Figure 4.14 assumes that LAPB is in use and that no previous I-frames have been transmitted.

Remember that as long as the I-frames are valid, the frame level will not

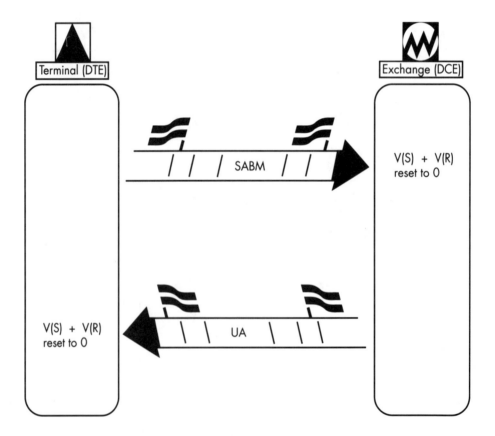

Figure 4.13 (a) With LAPB it is possible to set up the link with just one command (SABM) and one response.

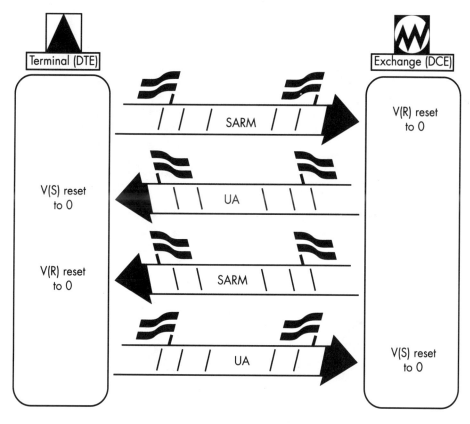

Figure 4.13 (b)   LAP needs two commands (SARM) and two responses.

be concerned about the data in the packet field; it is only really interested in transporting frames across the link.

In the example shown in Figure 4.14 the Exchange (DCE) acknowledges receipt of I-frames with the supervisory response 'Receiver Ready' (RR). For this reason it is called a 'supervisory acknowledgement'. If the Exchange (DCE) had information frames to send, it could have sent the acknowledgement within an I-frame rather than use the (RR) response. This is sometimes called a 'piggybacked' acknowledgement (Figure 4.15).

The busy condition

Under normal circumstances many frames will be transmitted rather than the few we have used in previous examples, especially when large quantities of data are being transmitted by the user. Quite often the receiving device

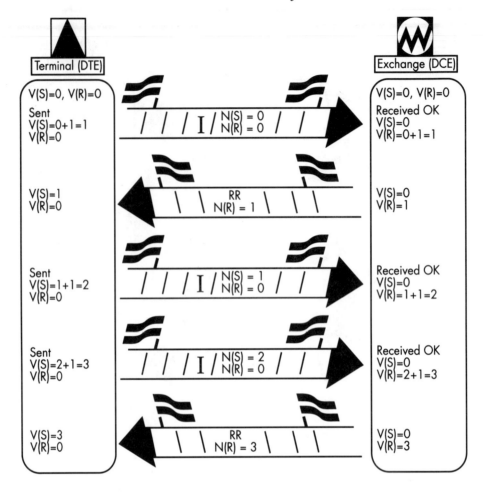

Figure 4.14 Information transfer: Each correctly received I-frame is acknowledged by a supervisory response (RR).

will temporarily be unable to handle any more incoming data. One common reason for this occurs when its temporary receiving storage area (i.e. its 'buffer') is full.

In Figure 4.16 we see a fairly simple example of a busy condition. The Terminal (DTE) wishes to transmit a quantity of I-frames and transmits the first frame. For one reason or another the Exchange (DCE) decides to go 'Busy' and sends the Exchange (DTE) an RNR frame. The Terminal (DTE) will start timer T1 and reset its transmission counter (N2).

If time T1 expires, the Terminal (DTE) has several options:

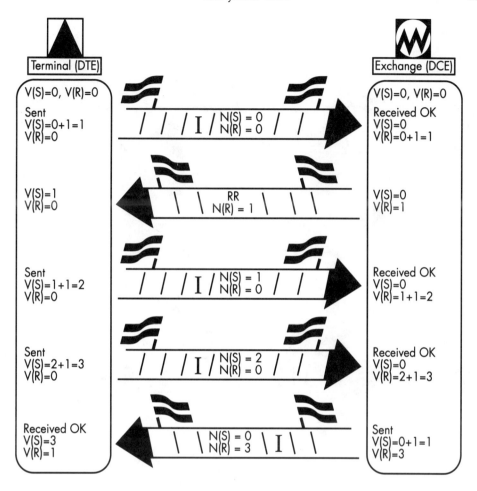

Figure 4.15 The DCE (Exchange) can transmit an I-frame together with the acknowledgement for any previously received I-frames from the DTE (Terminal). This is more efficient than acknowledging each I-frame with an (RR) response.

1. Under LAP it can poll the Exchange (DCE) by retransmitting its last unacknowledged I-frame.
2. Under LAPB it could transmit a supervisory command such as (RR), (REJ) or (RNR) with the Poll (P) bit set.

The busy device should still respond to supervisory commands and in this example it acknowledges the Poll with an (RNR) Frame that has its Final (F) bit set. The busy condition may be cleared at any time by the busy device transmitting a (REJ) or (RR) frame.

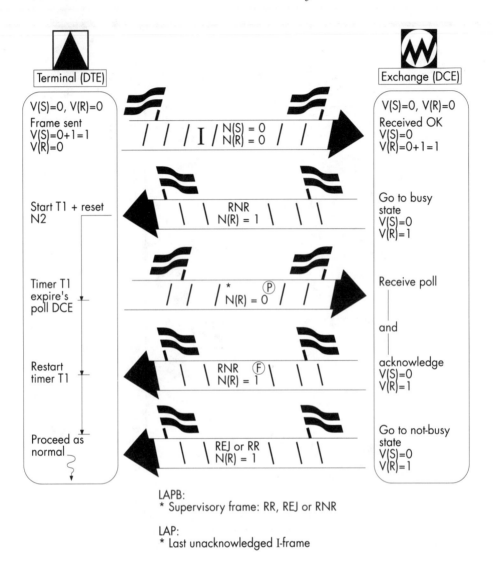

Terminal (DTE)

V(S)=0, V(R)=0
Frame sent
V(S)=0+1=1
V(R)=0

/ / / I / N(S) = 0
              N(R) = 0 / /

Start T1 + reset
N2

\ \ RNR \ \ \
     N(R) = 1

Timer T1
expire's
poll DCE

/ / / *   (P)
      N(R) = 0 / /

Restart
timer T1

\ \ RNR (F) \ \ \
     N(R) = 1

Proceed as
normal

\ \ REJ or RR \ \ \
     N(R) = 1

Exchange (DCE)

V(S)=0, V(R)=0
Received OK
V(S)=0
V(R)=0+1=1

Go to busy
state
V(S)=0
V(R)=1

Receive poll

and

acknowledge
V(S)=0
V(R)=1

Go to not-busy
state
V(S)=0
V(R)=1

LAPB:
* Supervisory frame: RR, REJ or RNR

LAP:
* Last unacknowledged I-frame

Figure 4.16   The busy condition where a DCE (Exchange) is sending RNR
frames because it is unable to receive any more I-frames.

If the busy device does not respond to polls, the N2 counter on the
transmitter will eventually reach its limit, causing the transmitter to attempt
to reset the link.

Frame level window

In X.25 the frame level 'window' represents the number (*K*) of sequentially numbered information frames that may remain unacknowledged by the receiver. The term 'frame level window' should not be confused with the 'packet level window' that has a similar function.

The total number of outstanding unacknowledged frames should never exceed seven. In practical terms, this means that the DTE or Exchange (DCE) will stop transmitting any more I-frames when V(S)=V(R) + *K*. Transmission will restart when outstanding acknowledgements are received.

Missing information frames

During its journey across the link a frame could be lost or corrupted during transmission, causing an FCS error at the receiver. There are two methods used at frame level to detect the loss of a frame:

1. By the use of sequence numbers: If an I-frame is lost during transmission, the send sequence number N(S) received would be out of sequence.
2. The transmitter uses a Timer (T1) to detect the loss of a frame. If an acknowledgement is not received within the time set by (T1) the transmitter will start to recover the lost frame.

Detecting an out of sequence frame

A reject (REJ) frame will be generated whenever an I-frame is received with a sequence number N(S) that is not the number expected. Any I-frames received after this will be scrapped by the receiver (see Figure 4.17).

Frame B could similarly have had an FCS error; the frame would be discarded by the receiver, creating the same effect as a lost frame.

Recovery of lost frames using transmission Timer (T1)

Whenever a command frame is sent, the transmitter will start a timer called T1. Time (T1) is the period that the transmitter is prepared to wait before it receives an acknowledgement for the command frame.

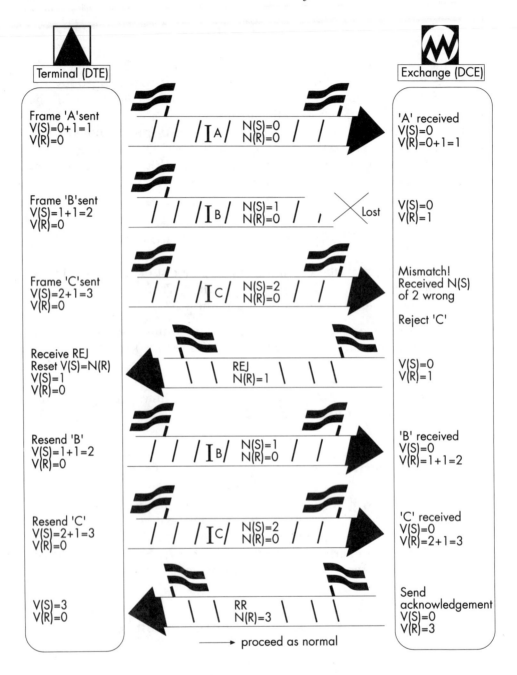

Figure 4.17 A reject (REJ) frame will be generated whenever an out of sequence I-frame is received.

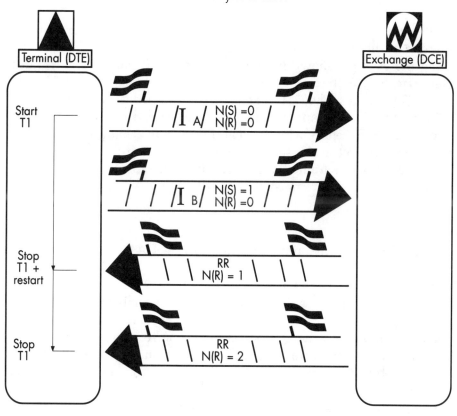

Figure 4.18 Timer (T1) is used to determine the time that a transmitter of a command frame is prepared to wait for an acknowledgement.

If an acknowledgement is received within the allotted time, T1 will be stopped and reset. If more commands are being transmitted, the timer will be left running until a suitable acknowledgement is received. If the time expires, the recovery procedures will be started. These differ between LAP and LAPB, basically because LAPB is capable of sending a supervisory command.

The following examples explain the concept in more practical terms.

Recovery of lost frame, using Timer (T1) – LAPB

The procedure for frame recovery under LAPB is slightly different from that under LAP because LAPB can send a supervisory frame as a command. The transmitter therefore has the capability of polling the receiver without transmitting an information frame (see Figure 4.19).

Using the example shown in Figure 4.18 the DTE transmits an I-frame and starts Timer (T1); the frame is lost or discarded because of an FCS error and Timer (T1) expires. The DTE is able to send a supervisory frame with its Poll (P) bit set to demand an immediate response from the Exchange (DCE). The Exchange (DCE) replies with its Final (F) bit set to acknowledge the poll, together with N(R) set to the sequence number it was expecting.

Upon receipt of this frame the DTE sets its own V(S) to match the value of the received N(R) and retransmits the lost I-frame.

Recovery of lost frame, using Timer (T1) – LAP

In this example the DTE has sent a frame with N(S)=2. The frame has either been lost in transmission or discarded by the receiver because of an FCS error; consequently an acknowledgement has not been sent. Timer T1 eventually times out and the DTE starts the frame recovery procedures.

In LAP an information frame is the only command frame available; the DTE therefore transmits an I-frame with the Poll (P) bit set to demand an immediate response from the Exchange (DCE).

In this particular case the Exchange (DCE) responds with a supervisory frame (RR) with the N(R) field set to (3) and with the Final (F) bit set to acknowledge the poll. Assuming the number is different from its own V(S) the DTE would reset V(S) to match the value of the received N(R) and restart transmission.

Recovery of lost acknowledgements, using Timer (T1)

So far Timer (T1) has been used to recover lost information (I) frames. The Timer (T1) may also be used to recover acknowledgements that have either been lost or discarded because of an FCS error.

In Figure 4.20 an I-frame has been sent, but an acknowledgement has not been received within the time required by Timer (T1). In this situation the transmitter may send a supervisory frame (RR in this case), with the Poll (P) bit set to demand an immediate response from the receiver. Upon receiving the (RR) frame, an (RR) response will be issued with the N(R) set to the receiver's current (R). The Final (F) bit is set to acknowledge the poll.

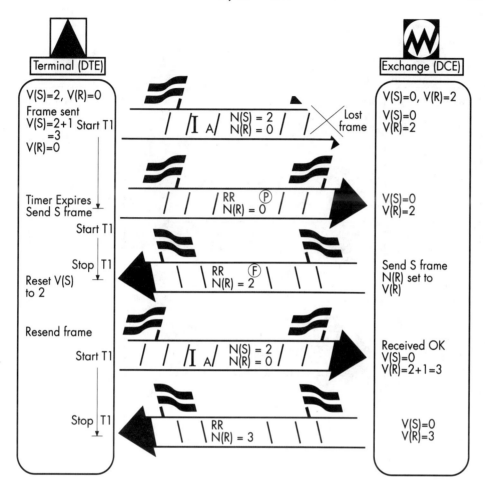

Figure 4.19 LAPB – recovering a lost frame using Timer (T1).

Link clear-down

Figure 4.21 shows the procedures for clearing the link down between the DTE (Terminal) and the DCE (Exchange). Once again we can see that the LAPB procedures are much simpler than those under LAP.

Questions

1. What are the four main functions of the frame layer?

2. What is HDLC an abbreviation for?

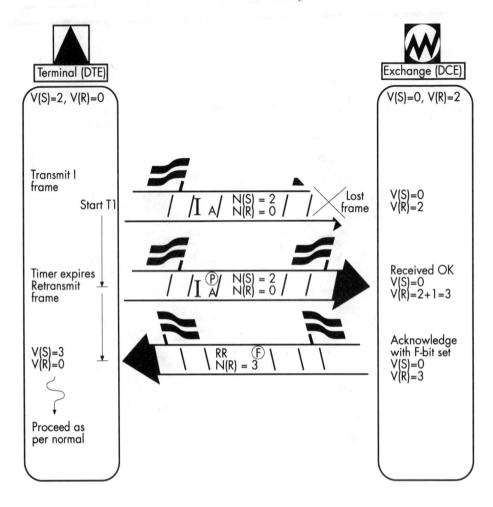

Figure 4.20   LAP – recovering a lost frame using Timer (T1).

3.   Name the six groups of data that make up an HDLC frame.

4.   What is the function of the address field in an HDLC frame?

5.   What is 'FCS' an abbreviation of, and what is its function?

6.   Name the different types of frame recommended in X.25.

7.   What are the following abbreviations short for:
(a) RR;
(b) REJ;
(c) RNR?

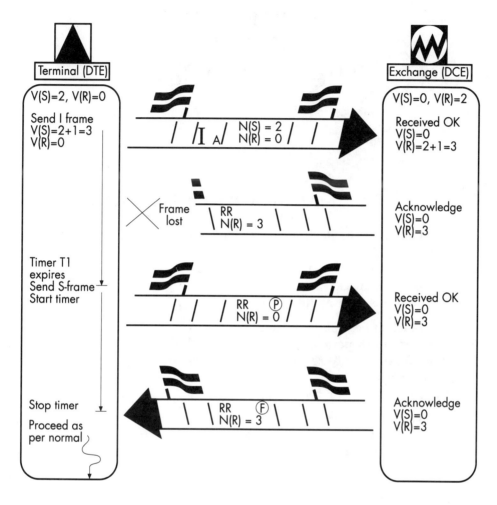

Figure 4.21 Recovery of a lost acknowledgement using Timer (T1).

8. What command is normally transmitted to request that a link be set up (assume LAPB is used)?

9. Name two methods of detecting lost frames.

10. What is the function of the following:
   (a) N(S);
   (b) N(R);
   (c) P (bit);
   (d) F (bit).

Chapter 5

The packet level

The function of the packet level

The packet level is the heart of the X.25 recommendation. Sometimes called level 3 or layer 3, it primarily provides procedures for the control of virtual circuits between the DTE (Terminal) and DCE (Exchange). Unlike the frame level (level 2), the packet level has 'end-to-end' significance (see Figure 5.1). These procedures include the following:

1. The establishment and clearing of virtual calls.
2. Management of permanent virtual circuits.
3. Provision of procedures for transferring packets.
4. Flow control.
5. Recovery from error conditions.

This sounds simple enough, but in reality the procedures used are quite complex and involved. The complexity is not helped by the similarity between the terms used at this level and the lower frame level. Readers

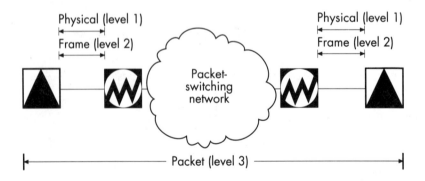

Figure 5.1   Unlike the frame and physical levels of X.25, the packet level has 'end-to-end' significance.

should ideally be familiar with the frame level procedures discussed in Chapter 4 before looking at the material covered in this chapter.

Virtual circuits

Virtual circuits were first mentioned in Chapter 2 where we encountered two types of virtual circuit; namely *switched* and *permanent*. Remember also that switched circuits are connections created when required, and last for the duration of a call. Permanent virtual circuits (PVCs) are literally a permanent connection between two users. A useful analogy of the difference between SVCs and PVCs is the comparison between ordinary telephone lines where the call is switched to the required destination, and a leased line where two telephones are permanently connected together.

Logical channels

A logical channel is a mechanism or technique that allows multiple, simultaneous virtual circuits to exist across one physical link between a user and the packet-switching network to which he or she is connected.

Each virtual circuit is given a unique number called the logical channel number (LCN). This number remains valid for the duration of the call. The LCN is attached to every packet associated with the call and differentiates these packets from those generated by other users. Many users are able to share the same physical link because the logical channel number allows the data to be *multiplexed*. The DTE (Terminal) or DCE (Exchange) will only transmit data when it has data to send; this is similar to *statistical time division multiplexing* (STDM), which is more sophisticated and efficient than *time division multiplexing* (TDM). These two terms sound fairly complicated but the theory is quite simple. It should always be remembered that the operation of the DTE (Terminal) and DCE (Exchange) is only *analogous* to STDM.

Imagine in Figure 5.2(a) that we are using two synchronized rotary switches. The left-hand switch will remain on the contact long enough to read off one character (A). Because the switches are synchronized the character (A) will be delivered to the correct contact at the other end of the communications link.

TDM is inherently inefficient as the rotary contacts always make contact whether a position has data to send or not. In practice, a TDM will use electronic circuits, not rotary switches. An STDM uses some complex algorithms (hence the term 'statistical') to ensure that the transmission

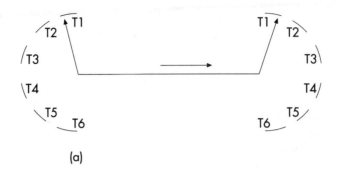

(a)

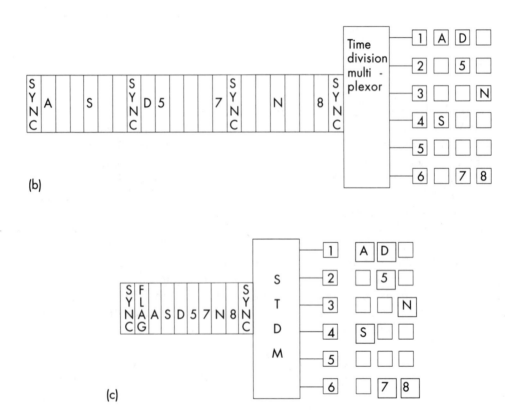

Figure 5.2 (a) The principle of time division multiplexing. (b) The receiving end of a time division multiplexor shows the empty and redundant slots that create inefficiency on the communications link. (c) The data compression facilities in a statistical time division multiplexor (STDM) provide efficient use of the communications link.

circuit is only used by devices that have data to send. An STDM may also strip out repetitive data during transmissions. This is called *data compression*.

Figure 5.2(b) shows the receiving end of a TDM; this equates to the right-hand side of Figure 5.2(a). A time slot is assigned to each channel regardless of whether it has data to send. The empty squares are wasting time on the communications link. Figure 5.2(c) shows an STDM that uses data compression techniques to carry data only from devices that are actively sending data.

Remember that LCNs allow us to *multiplex* the communications link. The numbering for logical channels only has significance between the user DTE (Terminal) and the DCE (Exchange). The network will assign its own numbers, and another numbering sequence will exist between the distant DCE (Exchange) and DTE (Terminal). It is important to realize that you could be connected on logical channel number X while your distant counterparty is on logical channel number Y. It is all too easy to think that logical channel numbers have end-to-end significance (Figure 5.3).

Logical channel assignment

The assignment of logical channel numbers follows the guidelines given in recommendation X.25. It is (in theory) possible to have 4095 logical channel numbers ranging from 0 to 4096, although 0 is reserved for restart and diagnostic information. In practice, the number of logical channels used does not normally exceed 255 and even this is rare. Why not use the full 4095 channel numbers? The answer here lies in the physical capabilities of the interface hardware. Remember from Chapter 2 that the DTE–DCE interface hardware consists of small, powerful computers. As the number of logical channels increases, the requirement for computer memory increases. There comes a point where it is neither practical nor feasible to use all 4095 channel addresses.

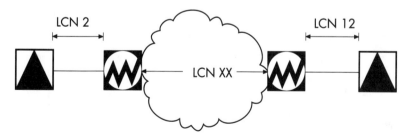

Figure 5.3 Logical channel numbers do not have end-to-end significance; a different number may exist at each end of the circuit, and within the network.

Logical channel types

Logical channels are gathered together into four main types:

1. PVC.
2. SVC – incoming only.
3. SVC – both ways.
4. SVC – outgoing only.

For each type of logical channel there are two logical channel groups, giving a total of eight logical channel groups (see Table 5.1).

The assignment of logical channel numbers (LCNs) is undertaken when the circuit is installed. Individual network suppliers can be quite flexible about the allocation of LCNs because they only have 'local' significance, i.e. between the DTE (Terminal) and DCE (Exchange). It would be possible to have a *call collision* if the DTE (Terminal) and DCE (Exchange) were both trying to initiate calls on the same LCN. To help overcome this problem, the DTE (Terminal) will always initiate a call on the *highest* LCN available, while the DCE (Exchange) must always use the *lowest*. A simple way of remembering this uses the 'T' in the term *DTE* to remind us that it starts from the *Top* number available.

Packets and packet headers

A *packet* is a block of user data with a *header* tagged on to it. A header is merely a string of data that refers to the packet. The contents of the header

Table 5.1 Logical channel assignment.

Logical channel type	Group number	First number in group
PVC	0	1
PVC	1	0
SVC – incoming only	2	0
SVC – incoming only	3	0
SVC – both ways	4	0
SVC – both ways	5	0
SVC outgoing only	6	0
SVC outgoing only	7	0

will vary depending on the type of packet. It may be remembered from Chapter 4 that all information is transported across the communications link in a *frame*. In Figure 5.4 we see that a packet of data is contained within the 'I' or 'information' field of an I-type frame.

Packet headers

All packet headers contain at least three common fields consisting of eight bits of data. (A block consisting of eight bits of data is called an *octet*.) These three octets form the packet header. The packet headers contain a large amount of information that relates to the particular packet. The first octet contains the *general format identifier* (GFI) which gives an indication of the general format (or layout) of the rest of the packet. The first octet also contains the *logical channel group number* (LCGN), which combines with the eight bits of the second octet to form the 12-bit logical channel number. The third octet contains the *packet type identifier* which identifies the type of

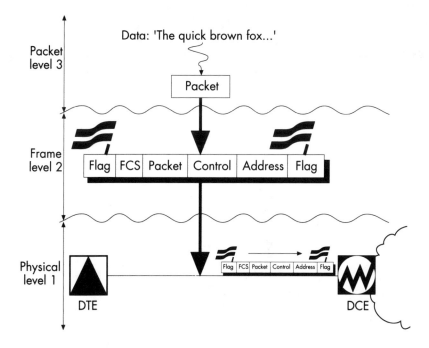

Figure 5.4 Packets generated at the packet level will be carried within the information frame generated at the frame level (Level 2), the complete frame being transmitted by the physical level.

packet in use. Altogether there are twenty different types of packet. These will be looked at individually shortly.

In books, the packet headers are usually displayed vertically instead of horizontally, allowing room to lay the information out in a clear and logical manner. The first bit of each octet that will be transmitted is shown on the right in Figure 5.5(a) and is called the *low order bit*.

Binary coding

An explanation of the packet headers assumes an understanding of *binary coding*. Taking Figure 5.6 as an example we see that an octet contains an example bit pattern of (00100101). The individual bits are numbered from right to left. Bit number 1 is called the *low order bit* and will be the first to be transmitted. The example shown in Figure 5.6 should be self-explanatory.

General format identifier

The *general format identifier* (GFI) is made up of four bits and literally indicates in general terms the type of packet associated with it. It identifies the general format (or layout) of the rest of the header.

Bit 8 is the *qualifier* (Q) bit. The Q bit is set to 1 to indicate that the packet contains higher level control information. The only higher level currently defined is X.29. See Chapter 7 for details of X.29.

Bit 7 is called the *delivery confirmation* (D) bit, and is used to determine

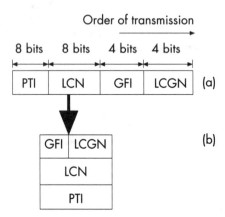

Figure 5.5 The packet header is common to all seventeen packet types: (a) shows order of transmission with the rightmost bit of the LCGN being first, while (b) illustrates the method used to show the packet header in books.

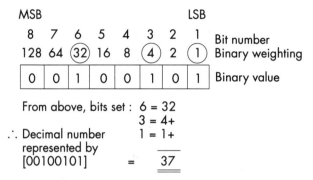

Figure 5.6 The bit pattern of [00100101] in the octet represents a decimal value of 37.

whether confirmation of packet delivery is made locally (i.e. between the local DCE and DTE) or *end-to-end* (i.e. between the two users on the network). Bit 7 will be set to 1 for local confirmation and to 0 for end-to-end confirmation.

Bits 3 and 4 of the GFI indicate whether a packet is using modulo 8 or 128 numbering. As we shall see shortly, all packets are assigned a sequence number. Modulo 8 numbering uses three bits to give a maximum of eight sequence numbers (0 through 7). Modulo 128 operation uses seven bits for sequence numbering allowing a maximum sequence number of 128 (0 through 127). (See Figure 5.7.)

Logical channel group number and logical channel number

A logical channel number is assigned to each virtual circuit when a call is established between two users, thereby allowing many virtual circuits to be supported on the same access link. It is important to remember that the LCN is only relevant between two adjacent nodes on a network and will not necessarily be the same throughout the network (see Figure 5.3).

Logical channel numbers

The logical channel group number (LCGN) and the logical channel number (LCN) both combine to form a 12-bit number that identifies a unique virtual circuit. This 12-bit number could *in theory* allow up to 4095 simultaneous virtual calls to be present at the packet level interface. This field can cause confusion when it is first looked at in detail. Many books glibly say that it is

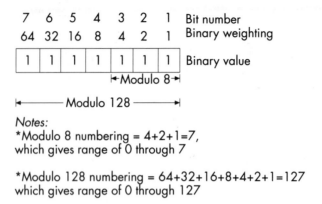

Notes:
*Modulo 8 numbering = 4+2+1=7,
which gives range of 0 through 7

*Modulo 128 numbering = 64+32+16+8+4+2+1=127
which gives range of 0 through 127

Figure 5.7 Explanation of modulo 8 and 128 numbering.

possible to have up to 4095 calls with little explanation of where this number comes from.

Figure 5.8 shows the 12-bit logical channel field with the binary value of each bit shown above it. Adding up all these values gives us 4096. Channel 0 is reserved, giving 4095 *possible* logical channels. It is rather confusing that this 12-bit number is made up of two fields with different names. Try to forget the term 'logical channel group number' and think of the whole field as being the 'logical channel number'.

Figure 5.8 shows an example of a logical channel field where the LCN is 12. This value is produced by setting bits 3 and 4. The binary values of these two bits (8 and 4 respectively) add together to make 12.

Packet type identifier

The *packet type identifier* (PTI) identifies the twenty individual packet types that may be used. The identifier is found in the headers of all packets; the make-up of this octet will be examined later in this chapter. Note that some networks (such as British Telecom's PSS) only use fourteen. The CCITT have made three of the packet types optional.

In Table 5.2 the twenty packet types are grouped according to their function. Note that the name of the packet type changes depending on its direction. For example, an outbound CALL REQUEST packet becomes an INCOMING CALL when it hits the distant end. Also note that three of the packet types are optional and will not be found on all networks. British Telecom's PSS network does not, for example, use the three optional packets, namely: RR (Modulo 128), RNR (Modulo 128) and Diagnostic.

Table 5.2 The packet types and their relevant groups. Note that three of the packet types will not be found on all networks.

Packet type		Octet 3 bits							
From DCE to DTE	From DTE to DCE	8	7	6	5	4	3	2	1
Call set-up and clearing									
Incoming call	Call request	0	0	0	0	1	0	1	1
Call connected	Call accepted	0	0	0	0	1	1	1	1
Clear indication	Clear request	0	0	0	1	0	0	1	1
DCE clear confirmation	DTE clear confirmation	0	0	0	1	0	1	1	1
Data and interrupt									
DCE data	DTE data	X	X	X	X	X	X	X	0
DCE interrupt	DTE interrupt	0	0	1	0	0	0	1	1
DCE interrupt confirm	DTE interrupt confirm	0	0	1	0	0	1	1	1
Flow control and reset									
DCE RR (MOD 8)	DTE RR (MOD 8)	X	X	X	0	0	0	0	1
DCE RR (MOD 128)*	DTE RR (MOD 128)*	0	0	0	0	0	0	0	1
DCE RNR (MOD 8)	DTE RNR (MOD 8)	X	X	X	0	0	1	0	1
DCE RNR (MOD 128)*	DTE RNR (MOD 128)*	0	0	0	0	0	1	0	1
	DTE REJECT (MOD 8)*	X	X	X	0	1	0	0	1
	DTE REJECT (MOD 128)*	0	0	0	0	1	0	0	1
Reset indication	Reset request	0	0	0	1	1	0	1	1
DCE reset confirm	DTE reset confirm	0	0	0	1	1	1	1	1
Restart									
Restart indication	Restart request	1	1	1	1	1	0	1	1
DCE restart confirm	DTE restart confirm	1	1	1	1	1	1	1	1
Diagnostic									
Diagnostic*		1	1	1	1	0	0	0	1
Registration									
	Registration request	1	1	1	1	0	0	1	1
Registration confirm		1	1	1	1	0	1	1	1

*Not necessarily available on every network.

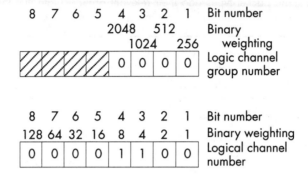

Figure 5.8 The LCN and LCGN combine to give a possible decimal value from 0 through 4095, giving (in theory) 4096 possible channel numbers. The example shows channel number 12.

The twenty different types of packet are grouped into six different categories:

1. Call set-up and clearing.
2. Data packets.
3. Interrupt packets.
4. Control and restart or clearing.
5. Diagnostic.
6. Registration.

Note that the last two groups contain optional packets that are not used on all networks.

Call set-up and clearing packets are used for the setting up and clearing of calls. They may sometimes contain user data.

Data packets are used solely for the transport of user data.

Interrupt packets are used to clear problems without completely resetting or restarting the virtual circuit.

Flow control and reset packets are only used for control purposes and contain no user data. Flow control packets ensure the smooth flow of data, while the reset packets literally reset the virtual circuit. The (RR) and (RNR) functions are similar to those at the frame level, except that the packet level frames have *end-to-end* significance, whereas at the frame level they only have *local* significance.

Unlike the interrupt function, a reset will completely reset the virtual circuit, possibly losing data that were being transmitted.

Diagnostic packets are optional. Their use is discussed below.

Registration packets are also optional and are discussed below.

The use and procedures of the packet level

The term *procedure* is frequently encountered in X.25. The *packet level procedures* determine the way that we use this part of the X.25 recommendation. For the moment let us move away from the complexities of packet switching and look at something more familiar – the telephone. There are many similarities between the procedures we use with the telephone and with the packet level procedures.

Let us take a simple example: you wish to have a telephone conversation with a friend who lives on the other side of the world. With the telephone you would pick up the receiver, and make a call using the correct number for your friend. Your friend would realize that there was an incoming call and answer the telephone, after which you would start the conversation. When you have both finished talking you would probably say goodbye and hang up your receiver.

There were three distinct phases of this routine operation:

1. Making the call.
2. Talking.
3. Disconnection.

These three phases are identical to those used in the packet level of X.25, namely:

1. Call establishment (or call set-up).
2. Disconnect or call-clearing phase.
3. Data transfer.

Each of the various phases in X.25 will now be examined, starting with call establishment.

Call establishment phase

A virtual call through a packet-switched network is initiated with a CALL REQUEST packet being transmitted by the local DTE (Terminal) (Figure 5.9). The packet identifies the destination address and the logical channel number that has been selected for the particular call. The packet may also contain information about any optional facilities and services that may be required. The packet can carry up to sixteen octets of user-provided data (call user data). If a feature called *Fast Select* is in operation, the packet can carry up to 128 octets of call user data.

The network will automatically route the CALL REQUEST to the exchange nearest to the distant user. The exchange will select a free logical

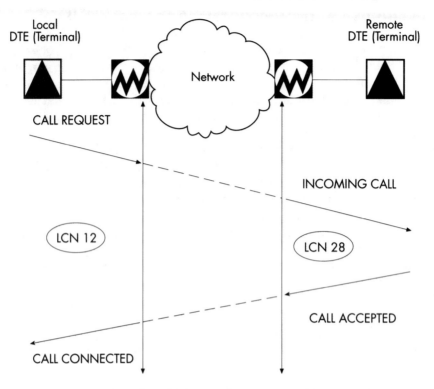

Figure 5.9   The call establishment phase is initiated by a CALL REQUEST packet from the local DTE (Terminal). Note that the LCNs only have local significance.

channel and send an INCOMING CALL REQUEST packet to the distant DTE (Terminal). If the distant user wishes to accept the call, the DTE (Terminal) will send a CALL ACCEPTED packet using the same LCN that the original call request came in on.

At this point the call establishment phase is complete and the two users may start to exchange data packets. There are some important points to remember here:

1.   Remember that the LCNs do not have *end-to-end* significance. LCNs are only relevant to the link between the DTEs (Terminals) and DCEs (Exchanges).

2. It is also worth noting how the name of the packets change on their way through the network. Note that an *outbound* CALL REQUEST packet becomes an *inbound* INCOMING CALL packet.

Before going any further it will be necessary to take a closer look at the call establishment packets; these particular packets have many features that are common to the other thirteen packet types.

CALL REQUEST/INCOMING CALL packet

The CALL REQUEST/INCOMING CALL packet shown in Figure 5.10 has components that are common to all packet types. The various fields will be looked at briefly, followed by a detailed look at their function. Remember that the first three octets are common to all packet types.

The general format identifier

This 4-bit field identifies the general format (or layout) of the rest of the header. (See pages 64, 65 for further details.)

The *LCN* field holds the LCN that has been selected for a particular call. Do not forget that the LCN only has *local significance*: the number will not necessarily be the same throughout the network.

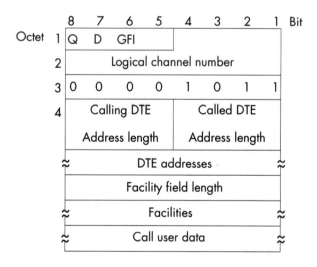

Figure 5.10 CALL REQUEST/INCOMING CALL packet. The first three octets are common to all packet types.

Octet 4 holds the *address length field* and contains in two *semi-octets* the length of the calling and called DTE addresses. (A semi-octet consists of four bits.) The octets that follow (maximum of fifteen) hold the actual DTE address. The subject of addressing will be discussed shortly.

The *facility length field* and *facilities field* contain information about option services; these, too, will be looked at later.

The last field in the CALL REQUEST packet is an area called the *call user data field*. This may hold up to sixteen octets of user data (128 octets if using the Fast Select). In this field the user may insert information that relates to the particular call, such as the log-on information if accessing a database. Fast Select is an option that is looked at on page 105.

Addressing

Users of a packet-switched network are allocated unique addresses (NUA – Network User Address) in much the same way that telephone numbers are given to subscribers. An example from the United Kingdom is British Telecom's bulletin board service for PSS. The bulletin board has an address of 23421920100515. (Note that this is a fourteen digit number.)

The CCITT X.121 recommendation is for public networks, and work is in hand to extend the recommendation to private networks. An address will consist of fourteen decimal digits made up of twelve mandatory and two optional digits.

Figure 5.11(a) shows how the numbers are allocated. The first four digits (2342) are called the DNIC (data network identification number). The first three (234) identify the country and the fourth the particular network within that country. The fourth digit of the DNIC plus eight more digits form the national number. This forms the unique address that is allocated to users when they initially come on to a particular network. The last two digits, 1 and 5 in the example 23421920100515, are used for *sub-addressing*. These are allocated by the user, not the network provider. These two digits are optional and may be generated when a call is made. They pass transparently through the network and may be the address for a particular application or program.

Figure 5.11(b) shows one possible application for sub-addressing. In this case a user has attached four printers to the DTE (Terminal). The printers are numbered A, B, C, D respectively. The *ports* on the DTE have different numbers assigned to them. Any data received with an address of 23421234567801 will go to printer A, similarly printer B will receive data with an address of 23421234567802. Another popular use for this facility is for accessing different programs or applications provided by a distant DTE.

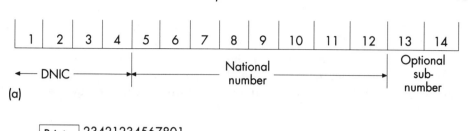

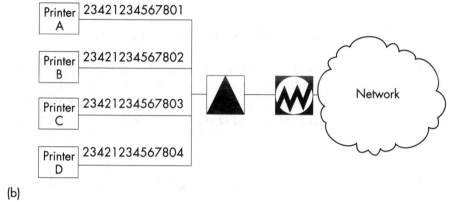

Figure 5.11 (a) The X.121 addressing format used with X.25. (b) The last two digits in the address can be used for sub-addressing. Here each printer is identified by a two-digit sub-address, i.e. 01 through 04.

The address fields

The address fields consist of three octets. These are combined to provide the following:

1. The address that is being called.
2. The address of the person making the call.
3. The length of both of the above fields.

The first octet of the address field is called the *address length field,* while the last two octets contain the *calling DTE address* and the *called DTE address.* The length field shows the address length in semi-octets and allows for variations in the lengths of address fields in various networks.

Facility field format

This octet contains optional parameters. Some may be selected by the caller when a call is made, and specify parameters that apply to the call. One good example here would be the use of *reverse-charging.* As with telephone networks it is possible to make reverse-charge, or 'call-collect', calls. This facility is often used on electronic mail systems where the vendor may pay for the cost of the call and recover the expense from usage charges.

Some of the other facilities available are relatively complex. The next chapter deals exclusively with an examination of the facilities provided within X.25.

CALL ACCEPTED/CALL CONNECTED packet

These two packets indicate that the DTE (Terminal) being called has accepted the call. Using the telephone analogy, we could say that CALL ACCEPTED equates to the distant telephone being answered. The DTE (Terminal) being called will generate a CALL ACCEPTED packet that will be delivered to the calling DTE (Terminal) as a CALL CONNECTED packet. After the call has been accepted the start of data transfer in both directions may start.

In Figure 5.9 we see where a call has progressed from the initial call being made with the CALL REQUEST packet to the call being acknowledged with a CALL ACCEPTED packet.

CALL ACCEPTED/CALL CONNECTED packet – format

The CALL ACCEPTED/CALL CONNECTED packet (Figure 5.12) has the first three octets that are found in all packets; these are the GFI, LCN and the packet type identifier. The address, facility and call user data fields are

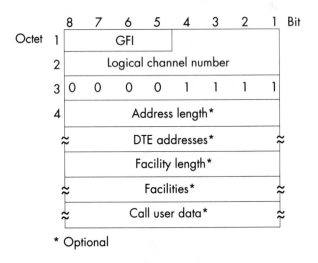

* Optional

Figure 5.12 Format of CALL ACCEPTED/CALL CONNECTED packet.

optional. A call user data field will only be present when the Fast Select facility is in use. In this case the field may contain a maximum of 128 octets of user data.

With CALL ACCEPTED packets the LCN will be assigned by the network. The CALL CONNECTED packet will have the same LCN that was assigned by the DTE (Terminal) that originated the call (see Figure 5.9).

CALL REFUSED and CALL NOT ESTABLISHED packets

Refusing an incoming call

Using the telephone analogy again, it is possible that the person at the distant end may not wish to answer the telephone. With X.25 the distant DTE (Terminal) will issue a CLEAR REQUEST to its associated DCE (Exchange). This is passed through the network and delivered to the calling DTE (Terminal) as a CLEAR INDICATE packet. The distant DCE (Exchange) will acknowledge the CLEAR REQUEST with a CLEAR CONFIRM packet (Figure 5.13).

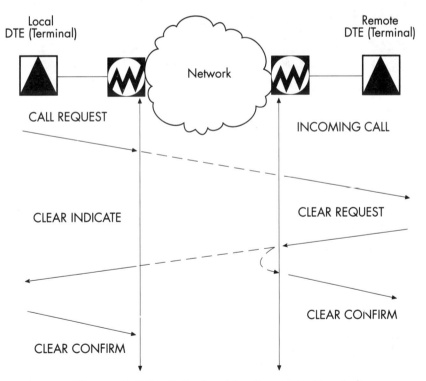

Figure 5.13 Call refused by distant DTE (Terminal).

Call not established

If for some reason the network wishes to cancel the call (e.g. if the network is busy), it will send the calling DTE (Terminal) a CLEAR INDICATE packet which should be acknowledged by the DTE (Terminal) with a CLEAR CONFIRM packet (Figure 5.14).

If a CALL REQUEST and INCOMING CALL packet are both trying to use the same logical channel number, the DCE (Exchange) that received the incoming call will cancel it and give priority to the CALL REQUEST packet.

Call-clearing phase

Going back to the ubiquitous telephone analogy, let us assume that our two subscribers have finished sorting out the world's problems and now wish to hang up. Under normal circumstances they would not just slam their receivers down but would follow a polite protocol. The same applies with X.25 where the call may be terminated or *cleared* by either user. Unlike the

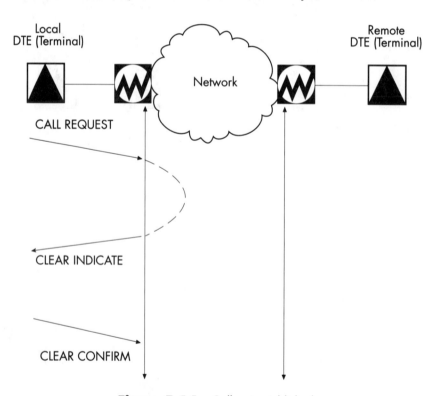

Figure 5.14   Call not established.

telephone network, it is possible for the packet-switching network to clear the call. This may be in response to technical problems and will cause the network to send an indication to both connected DTEs (Terminals) that it wishes to shut down the call.

It should be remembered that a clear only applies to the particular logical channel that is in use; it *does not* clear the whole link. (This could be done at the frame level with a DISC command.)

Call cleared by DTE (Terminal)

This is a straightforward situation where one user wishes to terminate the call, or 'hang up' to use the telephone analogy. In much the same way that a telephone user might say 'OK, goodbye – I'm going to hang up now', the DTE (Terminal) will transmit a CLEAR REQUEST packet to the DCE (Exchange). This in turn will be delivered to the distant DTE (Terminal) as a CLEAR INDICATION packet. The DCE (Exchange) connected to the DTE (Terminal) that originally decided to hang up will acknowledge the clear request with a CLEAR CONFIRM packet. Figure 5.15 makes this simple procedure clearer.

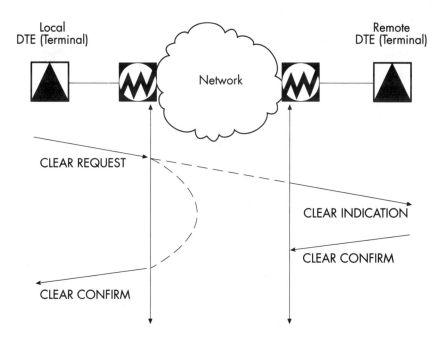

Figure 5.15 Call cleared by DTE (Terminal).

Call cleared by network

In Figure 5.16 we see the situation where the network wishes to clear the call. In this instance the network sends a CLEAR INDICATION packet to each of the DTEs (Terminals). These will in turn acknowledge with a CLEAR CONFIRM packet.

One point to note here is that the CLEAR CONFIRM packets generated by the two DTEs (Terminals) only have 'local' significance; in other words they are not transmitted through the network. Having said that, it is possible on some networks for these CLEAR commands to have 'end-to-end' significance, and the packets will be transmitted from the originating DTE (Terminal) through the network to the DTE (Terminal) at the distant end. It is also possible for a DTE (Terminal) still to be receiving incoming packets in the brief period between issuing a CLEAR REQUEST and receiving the CLEAR CONFIRM from its adjacent DCE (Exchange). In certain cases this could lead to a loss of data. This is an anomaly that will be discussed in the

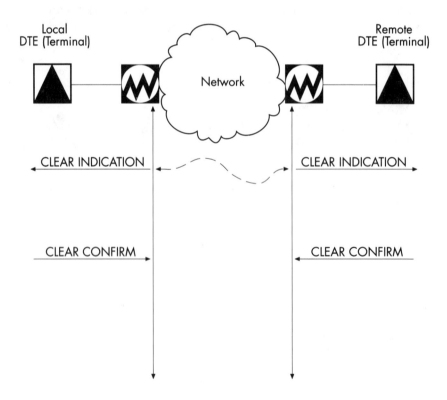

Figure 5.16   Call cleared by network.

next section. It should also be noted that a DTE (Terminal) can abort a call before it has even received a call connect packet.

Possible data loss

CLEAR REQUEST packets are not subject to flow control and it is therefore quite possible for one to reach its destination in advance of packets carrying live data. It is therefore essential that data transmission is closed down in a controlled manner before a clear request is issued. Remember the telephone analogy: people do not typically slam the telephone down at the end of a conversation; there is usually a brief 'winding up' conversation before replacing the receivers.

Call-clearing packet types

There are three packet types associated with call clearing. Two are issued by the DTE (Terminal) and the third by the DCE (Exchange).

1. CLEAR REQUEST is issued by a DTE (Terminal) when it wishes to terminate a call.
2. CLEAR INDICATE is generated by the network (DCE (Exchange)) when it wishes to close a call (possibly because of operational problems within the network).
3. CLEAR CONFIRM comes from a DTE (Terminal) to acknowledge a CLEAR INDICATE that may have been sent from the network.

Call-clearing packet format

Figure 5.17 shows the format of the three call-clearing packet types. The CLEAR CONFIRMATION packet is fairly straightforward but the CLEAR REQUEST/CLEAR INDICATION packet has two unfamiliar fields. These are *clearing cause* and *diagnostic code*. These three packets will now be examined.

The three call-clearing packets all contain the standard three header octets, with the general format identifier usually set to 0001, indicating that modulo 8 sequence numbering is being used. The LCN field will contain the logical channel number of the channel that is being cleared.

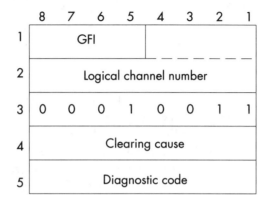

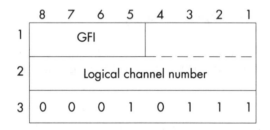

Figure 5.17   Call-clearing packet format.

An optional extended format is available. This provides optional address, facility and call user data fields. These may need to be used with optional facilities (e.g. Fast Select). These options are discussed at length in the next chapter.

The two unfamiliar fields used are the clearing cause and the diagnostic code.

Clearing cause field

This field quite simply gives the cleared DTE (Terminal) the reason for a call being cleared. When a DTE (Terminal) is raising a clear request it should set all the bits in the clearing cause field to 0. Failure to do this will result in a CLEAR INDICATION packet being sent by the DCE (Exchange).

If the network initiates a clear, the clearing cause field will contain the reason. The various clearing causes are listed in Table 5.3.

Table 5.3 Coding of clearing-cause field in clear indication packets. When bit 8 is set to 1, the bits represented by crosses (X) are those included by the distant DTE (Terminal) in the clearing or restart cause field of the CLEAR or RESTART REQUEST packet respectively.

	Bits							
	8	7	6	5	4	3	2	1
DTE originated	0	0	0	0	0	0	0	0
DTE originated	1	X	X	X	X	X	X	X
Number busy	0	0	0	0	0	0	0	1
Out of order	0	0	0	0	1	0	0	1
Remote procedure error	0	0	0	1	0	0	0	1
Reverse-charging acceptance not subscribed	0	0	0	1	1	0	0	1
Incompatible destination	0	0	1	0	0	0	0	1
Fast Select acceptance not subscribed	0	0	1	0	1	0	0	1
Invalid facility request	0	0	0	0	0	0	1	1
Access barred	0	0	0	0	1	0	1	1
Local procedure error	0	0	0	1	0	0	1	1
Network congestion	0	0	0	0	0	1	0	1
Not obtainable	0	0	0	0	1	1	0	1
RPOA out of order	0	0	0	1	0	1	0	1

Diagnostic field

The diagnostic field is optional in CLEAR REQUEST and CLEAR INDICATION packets. Its main purpose is to provide more information about the reason for the call being cleared. If a DTE (Terminal) wishes to clear a call it may send a clear request with the diagnostic field showing additional reasons for the clear. This field will be transmitted transparently through the network, and be delivered to the remote DTE (Terminal) in the CLEAR INDICATION packet.

There are about sixty diagnostic codes specified in X.25. They are listed in Appendix B.

Data transfer phase

The data transfer phase is where we start to see some useful data being transmitted through the network. (The point in our telephone analogy where a conversation takes place.) For the moment, let us assume that we wish to send a simple message to a distant user. For the sake of simplicity the message will be 'The quick brown fox jumps over the lazy dog's back.' In an X.25 data packet this data will be loaded into the user data field in Figure 5.4. The user data field is usually 128 octets long, but it is possible to have up to 4096 octets if this size has been successfully negotiated.

After a virtual circuit or call has been established between two DTEs (Terminals), the logical channel will enter the data transfer phase. Remember that a virtual circuit should really be called a 'switched virtual circuit' (SVC), and is similar to the connection made between two ordinary telephone subscribers who are connected via a dialled or 'switched' call. A permanent virtual circuit (PVC) will always be in the data transfer phase because the circuit between the two DTEs (Terminals) is always made. This is similar in concept to 'leased line' operation with telephones where the connection between the two subscribers is permanently made.

Structure of the X.25 data packet

The structure of the X.25 data packet is shown in Figure 5.18. The first three octets of the data packet header are already known: these are the general format identifier, logical channel group number and the logical channel number, and the packet type identifier. The GFI will have a 4-bit code – [QD01], where Q is the *Qualifier bit* and D is the *Delivery bit*.

Q-bit

When this is set to 0 the user data field will contain data intended for our distant user. If in our example Q=0, the field will have the 'Quick brown fox' message in it. With Q set to 1, the user data field will contain 'high level' control information. At the time of writing the only data of this sort would be X.29 control messages which are used in packet assembler/disassembler (PAD) operation.[1] A common use of this control information would be to set the distant PAD so that it always automatically inserts a line feed character when it receives a carriage return character from us.[2]

D-bit

As with the CALL REQUEST/INCOMING CALL packet, the D-bit is set to 0 for local acknowledgement of delivery, or set to 1 for acknowledgement

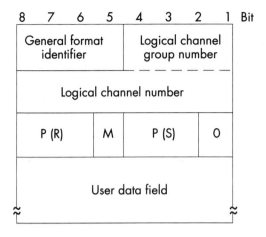

Figure 5.18 The structure of an X.25 DATA packet.

from the distant DTE (Terminal). The latter is called 'end-to-end' acknowledgement.

The DTE (Terminal) has the option of setting the D-bit to 1 either on individual packets or on all packets. Having the D-bit set on all packets will give maximum security but at the cost of extra delay.

M-bit

Bit 5 of octet 3 is called the *More (M) bit*. User data will often consist of a long stream of information that will not fit into one data packet. (A typical data packet has a maximum capacity of 128 bytes which is equivalent to 128 characters of ASCII text.) When set to 1 the M-bit indicates that the next packet to be sent is a logical continuation of the data in the current packet. The M-bit could also be set by the network if it has truncated one large packet into several smaller packets.

An example of the use of the M-bit is shown in Figure 5.19.

Packet sequence numbering

Octet three of the data packet has two fields called P(R) and P(S). These hold the *packet sequence numbers*. It is obviously desirable to have a numbering system for packets. The method employed here is similar to that used in the *frame level*, although it should be remembered that the packet level sequence numbers work independently of those assigned in the frame level.

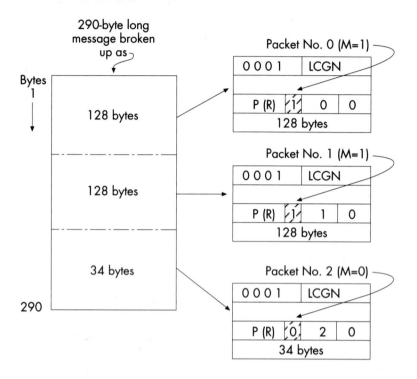

Figure 5.19 Use of the M-bit. A 290-byte message is carried in three packets. The M-bit is set in packets 0 and 1 to indicate that there is *more* data to come.

The *packet receive sequence number* P(R) indicates the number of the next packet that is expected from the distant user. The *packet send sequence number* P(S) is the number of the next packet to be sent.

Each packet is given a sequence number ranging from 0 to 7. The concept of using the numbering is fairly straightforward although it looks more complicated than it actually is. An example is shown in Figure 5.20.

Let us assume in Figure 5.20 that we have initiated a call, but have not yet transmitted or received any user data. P(S) and P(R) will both therefore be set to 0. User (A) sends a data packet with P(S)=0 and increments his own P(S) to 1. User (B) at the distant end is expecting to receive packet (0), thus matching the value of his own P(R) of (0). If user (B) accepts the packet he will increment his P(R) to 1. If for some reason he does not want the packet he could send a rejection (REJECT) packet to user (A) quoting the sequence number as a reference. *Remember*: this numbering system works in both directions.

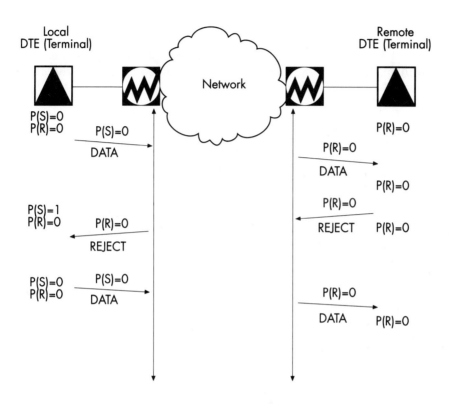

Figure 5.20 Use of the packet sequence numbers, P(R) and P(S). The distant DTE can request retransmission of packets by sending a REJECT with the P(R) set to the first packet number to be retransmitted.

There is an option for the modulo 8 count (i.e. 0 through 7) to be increased to modulo 128 (i.e. 0 through 127). If this option is in use, the GFI would have bit 6 set to 1 and a fourth octet tagged on to hold the 7-bit sequence numbers. The third octet would contain the packet sequence numbers P(S) and P(R).

Window size

So far we have simply stated that packets sent through the network merely need to be acknowledged. We have also assumed that any DTE (Terminal) sending packets will wait for an acknowledgement before sending any more packets. With X.25 a number of packets may be transmitted before an acknowledgement is received. This number is called the *window size*, and is usually between 1 and 7. The default is 2. This device improves the efficiency of the network as fewer acknowledgement packets need to be transmitted. The acknowledgement packets can be carried in control packets or in a data packet. Remember, though, that the acknowledgement is created by the transmitter receiving a P(R) number that is equivalent to the number of packets it has transmitted.

Flow control and retransmission

Supervisory packets

X.25 is a sophisticated recommendation that includes flow control and the ability to request retransmission. All this is achieved with the three *supervisory* packets RECEIVE READY (RR), RECEIVE NOT READY (RNR) and REJECT (REJ). The formats of these three packets are shown in Figure 5.21.

1. RECEIVE READY (RR): this packet quite simply indicates that the sender is ready to receive more packets. The value P(R) shows the next packet number expected and acknowledges receipt of all packets up to P(R–1). An RR packet is used when an acknowledgement is required but when there are no data packets being sent to *piggyback* the acknowledgement.

2. RECEIVE NOT READY (RNR): an (RNR) is sent by the DCE (Exchange) to tell the DTE (Terminal) that it should stop sending data as soon as possible. This packet will also acknowledge receipt of packets up to P(R–1). When the flow of data restarts, the first packet to be transmitted will have a P(S) equal to the P(R) sent in the RNR packet.

3. REJECT (REJ): the REJECT packet is used only by the DTE (Terminal) to request retransmission of one or several consecutively numbered packets starting with the packet number equal to the value of P(R) sent in the REJECT packet.

Interrupt procedure

The INTERRUPT packet

The orderly delivery of packets can sometimes cause problems that have been cleverly overcome by the use of an INTERRUPT packet. Take, for example, a situation where data packets have been sent and acknowledgements have not been received from the distant user. No indication has been given of an error or network problem. Under these conditions the DTE (Terminal) is stuck. It is unable to send more packets out to find out what is happening because it is still waiting acknowledgement of the previous data packets.

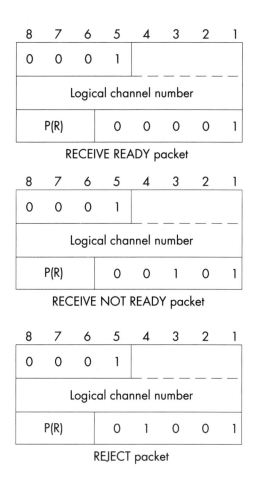

Figure 5.21 Structure of the three supervisory packets, RR, RNR and REJ.

It is possible to RESET the call using a procedure that will be discussed later. Unfortunately, this does exactly what it says and resets the sequence numbers, so possibly losing any unacknowledged data packets that are already stuck in the system. The interrupt packet can overcome the need to RESTART, and is a cunning way of getting round a serious problem.

An INTERRUPT packet does not have a sequence number and may be thought of as a privileged or 'express delivery' packet. The interrupt will have priority over other data packets that are awaiting delivery and does not affect the status of the call that is in progress. The ability to interrupt is a good example of the subtlety and sophistication that has been built into the X.25 recommendation.

The layout of the INTERRUPT and INTERRUPT CONFIRMATION packets is shown in Figure 5.22. The INTERRUPT packet consists of four octets; the fourth octet being a user data field. The data in this field are completely ignored by the network and pass transparently through to the distant end. Given its diminutive size of one octet, the field is obviously intended to carry a pre-arranged code. If the contents of the field are greater than one octet the network will reset the call.

An acknowledgement of an INTERRUPT, called an INTERRUPT CONFIRMATION must be received before the network will accept any more INTERRUPT packets.

Virtual circuit reset procedures

During the data transfer phase it may be necessary to reinitialize the flow control or sequence numbering on a particular switched virtual circuit (SVC), or permanent virtual circuit (PVC). The reset may be initiated either by the Terminal (DTE) or the Exchange (DCE). It may have local or end-to-end significance depending on the option selected.

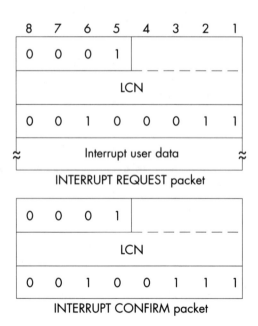

Figure 5.22   Structure of the INTERRUPT REQUEST and INTERRUPT CONFIRM packets.

Application of a reset is a last, desperate effort to recover from an error situation, and should always be used with extreme caution. Reset will cause all sequence numbers P(R) and P(S) to be zeroed and any unacknowledged data packets (i.e. those still on their way) will be discarded by the network.

RESET initiated by DTE (Terminal)

If a DTE wishes to reset the call it will send a RESET REQUEST packet into the network together with a RESET REASON code, the latter being placed in the *cause field* (see Figure 5.23). The reset will be acknowledged by the Exchange (DCE) with a RESET CONFIRM packet. The remote DTE (Terminal) will receive a RESET INDICATE packet from the network that should be acknowledged with RESET CONFIRM.

RESET initiated by DCE (Exchange)

If the network wishes to invoke a reset it will send RESET INDICATE packets to both DTEs (Terminals). These will acknowledge with RESET CONFIRM packets (Figure 5.24).

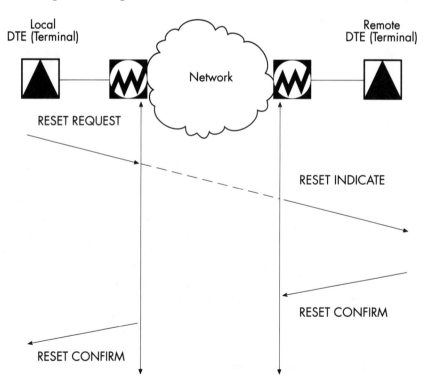

Figure 5.23 RESET initiated by DTE (Terminal).

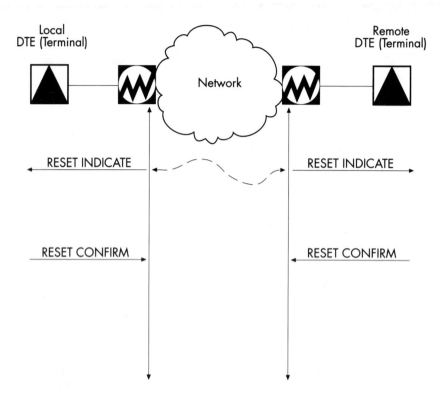

Figure 5.24   RESET initiated by the network, DCE (Exchange).

Looking closely at the two packets in Figure 5.25 we see that the GFI would be [0001] for modulo 8 numbering. The logical channel number field shows the number of the virtual circuit or call that is being reset. If we were communicating on LCN 27 and the network initiated a *reset*, the LCN of the RESET REQUEST packet would be 27. The packet type is indicated in the third octet, i.e. [00011011] for a REQUEST/INDICATION packet, and [00011111] for RESET CONFIRM packet.

We would obviously like to know the reason for any circuits being reset. The reason for a reset is contained in the *resetting cause* field of the RESET REQUEST packet. The cause field will be set to zero when the reset is instigated by the remote DTE (Terminal). The DTE that initiates the reset is allowed to add one octet of user data known as the *diagnostic* octet. This will be passed to the remote DTE (Terminal) to provide additional information about the reset.

If the network initiates a reset, the cause field will be set to a non-zero

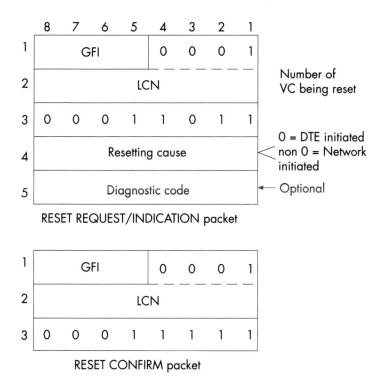

RESET REQUEST/INDICATION packet

RESET CONFIRM packet

Figure 5.25 Structure of RESET packets.

value, with this number indicating the reason for the reset. These are shown in Table 5.4.

RESTART procedures (packet level)

The format of the RESTART packets is shown in Figure 5.26. The RESTART procedure is used to clear simultaneously *all* the virtual circuits that are in use on a link between a DTE (Terminal) and DCE (Exchange). This means that up to 4095 virtual circuits or calls could be cleared if a RESTART procedure is initiated. It may be used at any time and will typically be used to recover from a major DTE (Terminal) or network, DCE (Exchange), failure. Remember that a RESTART will clear *all* circuits, whereas RESET only clears one particular circuit (see Figure 5.27).

Table 5.4 Coding of reset cause field in RESET INDICATION packet generated by the network, DCE (Exchange). When bit 8 is set to 1, the bits represented by crosses (X) are those indicated by the remote DTE (Terminal) in the resetting cause field (SVCs and PVCs) or the resetting cause field (PVCs) of the RESET or RESTART REQUEST packet, respectively.

	Bits 8	7	6	5	4	3	2	1
DTE originated	0	0	0	0	0	0	0	0
DTE originated	1	X	X	X	X	X	X	X
Out of order	0	0	0	0	0	0	0	1
Remote procedure error	0	0	0	0	0	0	1	1
Local procedure error	0	0	0	0	0	1	0	1
Network congestion	0	0	0	0	0	1	1	1
Remote DTE operational	0	0	0	0	1	0	0	1
Network operational	0	0	0	0	1	1	1	1
Incompatible destination	0	0	0	1	0	0	0	1
Network out of order	0	0	0	1	1	1	0	1

	8	7	6	5	4	3	2	1 Bits
1	GFI				0	0	0	0
2	0	0	0	0	0	0	0	0
3	1	1	1	1	1	0	1	1
4	Restart cause							
5	Diagnostic code							

RESTART REQUEST/INDICATION packet

1	GFI				0	0	0	0
2	0	0	0	0	0	0	0	0
3	1	1	1	1	1	1	1	1

RESTART CONFIRM packet

Figure 5.26 Format of RESTART packets.

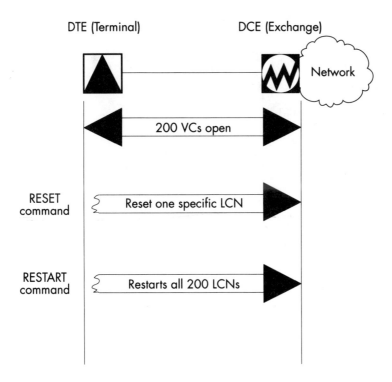

Figure 5.27 Differences between RESET and RESTART: The RESET procedure resets one virtual circuit on a link. A RESTART procedure clears *all* circuits.

The RESTART procedure is usually used when the packet level is being set up, thereby clearing any circuits and initializing the link. In extreme circumstances it will be used for recovering from a major fault condition.

RESTART initiated by DTE (Terminal)
A DTE (Terminal) will initiate a RESTART by transmitting a RESTART REQUEST packet to the DCE (Exchange) (Figure 5.28). The DCE acknowledges with a RESTART CONFIRM packet and will immediately transmit a CLEAR INDICATE packet to all the remote DTEs (Terminals) that have a virtual circuit connected with the DTE (Terminal) that instigated the RESTART.

RESTART initiated by network
A RESTART may also be invoked by the network. In this case the network will ensure that the relevant DCEs (Exchanges) transmit a CLEAR

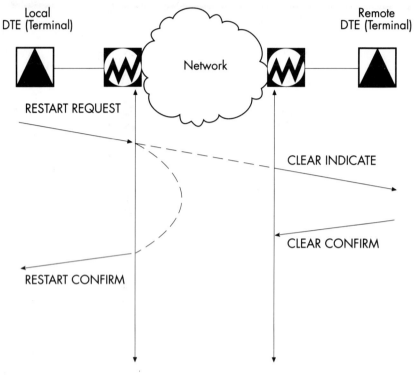

Figure 5.28   RESTART initiated by DTE (Terminal).

INDICATE packet to the DTEs (Terminals) associated with the virtual
circuits being restarted (Figure 5.29).

The diagnostic packet

The diagnostic packet shown in Figure 5.30 is optional and some networks
such as PSS do not use it. The diagnostic packet can recover a particular
failure where other methods such as RESET have either failed or been
inappropriate. A diagnostic packet may, for example, be used when a DTE
(Terminal) transmits an invalid packet or may have used an unassigned
logical channel number. Diagnostic packets will only be issued by the DCE
(Exchange) and on logical channel (LCN) 0. The receiving DTE (Terminal)
does not have to acknowledge receipt of the diagnostic.

The fourth octet in Figure 5.30 contains the *diagnostic code* that gives a
reason for the packet being issued. Appendix B of this book identifies about
sixty reasons, derived from Appendix E of the 1984 X.25 recommendation.
Some examples from this list are:

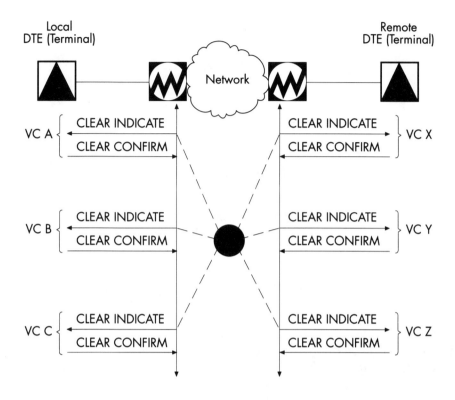

Figure 5.29   RESTART initiated by network.

Invalid packet type   0 0 0 1 0 0 0 0
Invalid LCN   0 0 1 0 0 1 0 0

The fifth octet contains a *diagnostic explanation* that will contain the first three octets (i.e. header) of an erroneous packet, or whatever bits received if shorter than three octets. When the diagnostic packet is issued because of a DCE (Exchange) time-out, the explanation field will consist of two octets coded to show the following:

1. Bits 8, 7, 6, 5 of octet one contains the GFI for the connection.
2. Bits 4 through 1 of octet one and bits 8 through 1 of the second octet will be set to 0 if Timer T10 has expired. The same bits will contain the LCN on which the time-out occurred if Timers T12 or T13 have expired. (See next paragraph for an explanation of the timers mentioned here.)

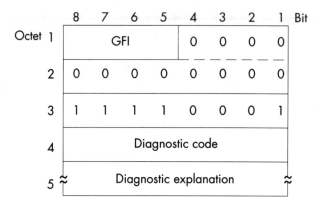

Figure 5.30 Structure of diagnostic packet.

Timers used in X.25

Timers are frequently employed in communications systems; they serve a variety of purposes but are usually used to initiate recovery from an error condition. A good example here is the timer used to disable a telephone line when the handset has been accidentally left off the hook. In X.25 the timers are grouped according to whether they are monitored by the DCE (Exchange) or the DTE (Terminal). In terms of X.25, a DCE (Exchange) time-out is the maximum amount of time available for the DTE (Terminal) to perform a particular function. Be aware, however, that the implementation may vary between individual networks. Table 5.5 lists the more frequently encountered timers together with a note of the response required.

Questions

1. What is the most significant difference between the packet layer and the other two layers of X.25?

2. Name the five main procedures associated with the packet level.

3. What are 'logical channels' used for? What significance do they have across the network?

4. Name the type of frame used to transport 'packet data'.

5. Name the different types of packet.

6. What is the function of the Q-bit and the D-bit?

7. Name the six different categories of packet types.

Table 5.5 Timers used at packet level.

Timer	Function	Duration (secs)	Action
(a)	Timers used by the DCE (Exchange)		
T10	RESTART INDICATION response	60	Send DIAGNOSTIC
T11	INCOMING CALL response	180	Send CLEAR
T12	RESET INDICATION response	60	Send CLEAR
T13	CLEAR INDICATION response	60	Send DIAGNOSTIC
(b)	Timers used by the DTE (Terminal)		
T20	RESTART REQUEST response	180	Retransmit RESTART
T21	CALL REQUEST response	200	Send CLEAR
T22	RESET REQUEST response	180	Send CLEAR
T23	CLEAR REQUEST response	180	Retransmit CLEAR

8. What are the three main phases of call establishment on an X.25 interface?

9. What is an NUA? Name its three sections.

10. List the different types of CLEAR packet.

11. Explain the term 'windowing'. Give its default, minimum and maximum values.

12. What is an 'INTERRUPT packet' and how can it be used?

13. Explain the difference between RESET and RESTART.

Notes

1. A PAD acts as protocol converter, allowing 'dumb' or character terminals to interface into a packet-switched network.
2. Recommendation X.29 is discussed on pp. 138–40 in Chapter 7.

Chapter 6

X.25 facilities

What is a facility?

In simple terms, an X.25 facility allows the user to do something other than just transmit and receive data in a high speed and virtually error-free environment. In the terminology of the X.25 recommendation, facilities are referred to as 'options'. A convenient analogy here is provided by a telephone network. Telephone networks were originally very simple in operation, providing simple communications for most users. In time someone decided that it would be useful to provide additional features such as 'reverse-charging', or 'call-collect' as it is known in the United States. This is a *facility* on the telephone network.

Some of the facilities on a telephone network are invoked when a subscriber signs up with the telephone company and others are provided for individual calls. In other words, the facilities may be provided at *subscription time* or on a *per call* basis. The facilities recommended within X.25 are implemented in much the same way. It is possible to make a telephone call from London to New York that bridges several different telephone networks even though the network in New York may offer facilities that are not available in London. On an international scale the telephone companies will have to provide certain facilities that must always be available and are said to be *mandatory*. Others, though, may not be mandatory and would be *optional* but standard world-wide. Others may be peculiar to one particular telephone network and only available to its own subscribers. These are therefore said to be *network-dependent*.

Most of the facilities provided within X.25 are self-explanatory, but some will need further explanation. Good examples here are *reverse-charging* which is simple enough, but *D-bit modification* does not instantly reveal its purpose. The various facilities are invoked by coding a *facilities field* within a CALL REQUEST packet. This will be received by the distant user as an INCOMING CALL REQUEST packet. If facilities are not required the field need not be present. The detailed format of this field will be looked at shortly.

The X.25 facilities fall into four general groups or classes:

1. International facilities that are found in CCITT recommendation X.2.[1] These are divided into two classes: essential and additional or optional. The essential facilities are mandatory on all public data networks, while the optional facilities will only be found on certain networks.

2. Facilities that are only offered by the local network through which the call originated (i.e. the calling network).

3. Facilities that are only offered by the network that is being called (i.e. the distant network).

The last type of facility is called a 'national' facility:

4. CCITT-specified facilities for the DTE (Terminal). These were new in the 1984 version of the X.25 recommendation.

The international facilities are referred to as being either 'essential' or 'additional'. The essential facilities are mandatory on all networks while the additional facilities may be provided at the option of individual networks.

The DTE facilities in 4 enable a DTE (Terminal) to request particular services or functions from the distant DTE (Terminal) that is being called. These particular facilities will be discussed in the next chapter.

The facilities available in 1 and 2 above, may be either arranged when the user signs up with the network (i.e. at *subscription time*), or specified when a particular call is made (i.e. on a *per call basis*).

Table 6.1 lists the facilities that are available for use with virtual circuits and permanent virtual circuits. In Table 6.2 the coding of the facility code fields and the packet types in which they may be used are shown (remember that this table is only required for the per call facilities).

Invoking facilities

It should be remembered that these facilities are only available at the *packet* level. The X.25 facilities are invoked by inserting a special code in the *facility length field* within a CALL REQUEST packet.[2] This field follows immediately after the *address field*. The facility length field always contains at least one octet that identifies the number of octets that make up the rest of the facilities section, to a maximum of 63 octets (see Figure 6.1). Only the first six

Table 6.1   X.25 facilities.

Facility	VC	PVC
(a) Optional user facilities assigned for an agreed contractual period		
Incoming calls barred	E	
Outgoing calls barred	E	A
One-way logical channel outgoing	E	
Flow control parameter negotiation	E	
Closed user group	E	
Fast Select acceptance	E	
Throughput class negotiation	E	
On-line facility registration	A	
Extended frame sequence numbering	A	A
Extended packet sequence numbering	A	A
D-bit modification	A	A
Packet retransmission	A	A
One-way logical channel incoming	A	
Non-standard default packet sizes	A	A
Non-standard default window sizes	A	A
Reverse-charging acceptance	A	
Local-charging prevention	A	
Network user identification	A	
Charging information	A	
Recognized private operating agency (RPOA) selection	A	
Hunt group	A	
Call redirection	A	A
Default throughput class assignment	A	A
Multilink procedure	A	
CUG with outgoing access	A	
CUG with incoming access	A	
Incoming calls barred within user group	A	
Outgoing calls barred within user group	A	
Bilateral CUG	A	
Bilateral CUG with outgoing access	A	
(b) Optional user facilities on a per call basis		
CUG selection	E	
Flow control parameter negotiation	E	
Fast Select	E	
Throughput class negotiation	E	
Transit delay selection and indication	E	
Bilateral closed user group selection	A	
Reverse-charging	A	
RPOA selection	A	
Charging information	A	
Call redirection notification	A	
Called line address modification notification	A	
Network user identification	A	
CUG with outgoing access selection	A	

E =   Essential service or facility to be offered on all networks.
A =   Additional user service or facility that may be offered by some networks.
VC =   Only applicable when virtual call service is in use.
PVC =   Only applicable when permanent virtual call service is in use.

Table 6.2 Coding of the facility code field.

Facility	Packet types in which it may be used							Facility code — Bits							
	CALL REQUEST	INCOMING CALL	CALL ACCEPTED	CALL CONNECTED	CLEAR REQUEST	CLEAR INDICATION	DCE CLEAR CONFIRMATION	8	7	6	5	4	3	2	1
Flow control parameter negotiation	X	X	X	X											
– packet size								0	1	0	0	0	0	1	0
– window size								0	1	0	0	0	0	1	1
Throughput class negotiation	X	X	X	X				0	0	0	0	0	0	1	0
Closed user group selection	X	X													
– basic format								0	0	0	0	0	0	1	1
– extended format								0	1	0	0	0	0	1	1
Closed user group with outgoing access selection	X	X													
– basic format								0	0	0	0	1	0	0	0
– extended format								0	1	0	0	1	0	0	0
Bilateral closed user group selection	X	X						0	1	0	0	0	0	0	1
Reverse-charging	X	X						0	0	0	0	0	0	0	1
Fast Select	X	X						0	0	0	0	0	0	0	1
Network user identification	X		X					1	1	0	0	0	1	1	0
Charging information: – requesting service	X		X					0	0	0	0	0	1	0	0
– receiving information					X	X	X			Further study					
monetary unit								1	1	0	0	0	1	0	1
distance								1	1	0	0	0	1	0	1
segment count								1	1	0	0	0	0	1	0
call duration								1	1	0	0	0	0	0	1
RPOA selection – basic format	X							0	1	0	0	0	1	0	0
– extended format								1	1	0	0	0	1	0	0
Called line address modified notification			X	X	X	X		0	0	0	0	1	0	0	0
Call redirection notification		X						1	1	0	0	0	0	1	1
Transit delay selection and indication	X	X		X				0	1	0	0	1	0	0	1

Source: CCITT Recommendation X.25, 1984.

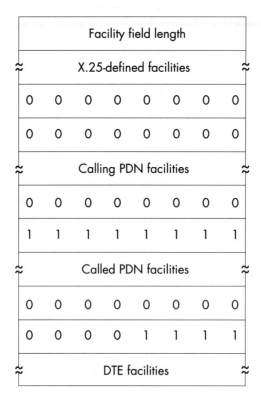

Facility field length
X.25-defined facilities
0 0 0 0 0 0 0 0
0 0 0 0 0 0 0 0
Calling PDN facilities
0 0 0 0 0 0 0 0
1 1 1 1 1 1 1 1
Called PDN facilities
0 0 0 0 0 0 0 0
0 0 0 0 1 1 1 1
DTE facilities

Figure 6.1   The facilities field within a CALL REQUEST packet.

bits of this field need to be transmitted; the last two bits are therefore set to zero. If special facilities are not required, the facility field length will be set to 2, and the network will insert the code (0100) to indicate no *reverse-charging* or *minicall*. (These terms will be explained shortly.)

The facilities are specified by a facility code in bits 1 to 6 that identifies the individual facilities. The high order bits (7 and 8) indicate the number of octets that are in the facility parameter field (see Figure 6.2). The coding of the parameter length field is as follows:

00 – One octet follows in the parameter field. This is known as a *class A* facility.

01 – Two octets follow in the parameter field. This is known as a *class B* facility.

10 – Three octets follow in the parameter field. This is known as a *class C* facility.

11 – More than three octets follow in the parameter field. This is known as a *class D* facility, and is a variable length field.

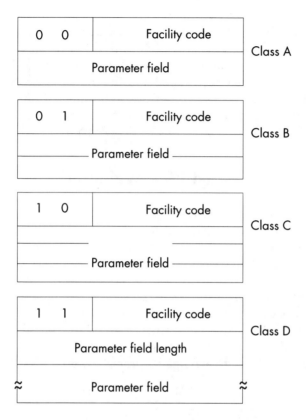

Figure 6.2 Facility formats showing the four different classes of facility.

Note that the class D field is a variable length field: the octet following the code indicates the size of the parameter field in octets.

Coding the facilities

The facility codes are binary coded. The six bits in each code gives 64 facility codes for the four classes A, B, C and D. Four classes with 64 codes each give a total possible number of facilities of 255 (0 through 255 = 256).

Facility markers

It is possible that a user may wish to invoke facilities from different categories (e.g. one that is provided on his or her local network together with an international facility). In this case the international facilities specified by X.2 are given first, followed by the other categories required. In Figure 6.3 we see that a facility marker, coded with zeros, is used to separate the calling and called public data network fields. The octet that follows immediately after the marker is used to differentiate between the calling and called facilities. If this field is all zeros it identifies national facilities for the calling network. When coded to all ones it marks the national facilities for the network that supports the called DTE (Terminal).

Facilities available

As stated earlier the facilities available are divided into two groups. The first requires arrangements to be made at subscription time (i.e. when the user signs up with the network). The second group of facilities are available on a per call basis (i.e. may be used on particular calls and do not need prior arrangements to be made). For example, any attempt to use a subscription-type facility without prior arrangement will result in the DCE (Exchange) issuing a CLEAR INDICATION packet with a clearing cause of *facility not subscribed*.

    The facilities discussed here are not listed in any particular order of importance, although they do basically follow the order of the X.25 recommendation. They are arranged primarily more for ease of understand-

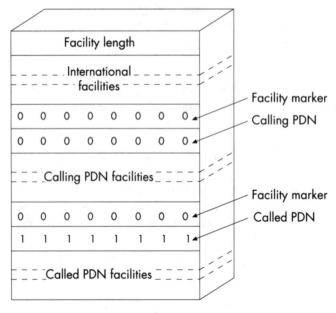

Figure 6.3   Facility marker formats.

ing than any other concern. Reference should always be made to Table 6.1 to determine whether the facilities are available at subscription time or on a per call basis.

Fast Select

Fast Select is available on a per call basis and is an optional facility that typifies the power and efficiency of X.25. With conventional communications systems the user would normally have to initiate a call and receive a 'connected' or go-ahead message before he or she could transmit any data. Fast Select allows the user to include data in the initial CALL REQUEST packet. This feature is particularly useful in a case such as credit card checking. In this instance, the user will initiate a call to the credit card computer and include within that CALL REQUEST packet up to 128 octets of information. This could be the name of the card holder together with details of the transaction. Fast Select establishes high speed and efficient usage of the communications network.

Fast Select may be used with CALL REQUEST, CALL ACCEPTED and CLEAR REQUEST packets.

Invoking Fast Select

The Fast Select facility uses the same field as reverse-charging (the use of the latter is self-explanatory but will be discussed below). Bit 8 set to '1' will indicate that Fast Select is in use while bit 7 set to either '1' or '0' will indicate whether Fast Select is selected with *unrestricted response* (0) or *restricted response* (1). With restricted response, the DTE (Terminal) that is being called is restricted to respond with the transmission of a CLEAR REQUEST packet. Unrestricted response allows any valid type of response.

These two types of response generate two different types of Fast Select calls. These are *Fast Select with immediate clear* (using restricted response) and *Fast Select with data transfer* (using unrestricted response). These two items will now be discussed together with relevant diagrams in Figures 6.4 and 6.5 respectively.

Fast Select with immediate clear

In Figure 6.4 a user will generate a CALL REQUEST with the facility field coded thus:

Bits:	8	7	6	5	4	3	2	1
Value:	1	1	0	0	0	0	0	0

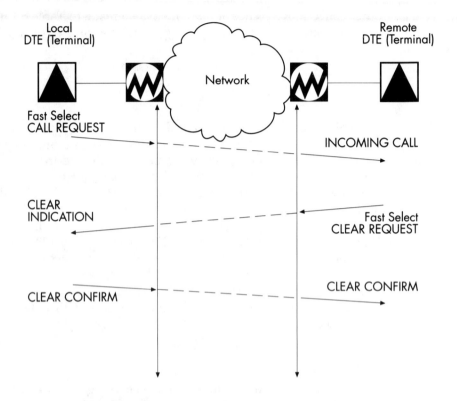

Figure 6.4   Fast Select with immediate clear.

The user data fields in the CALL REQUEST packet can contain up to 128 octets of user data. Upon receipt, the distant Terminal (DTE) will issue a CLEAR REQUEST packet that may also contain up to 128 octets of user data. This is acknowledged by the originating DTE (Terminal) with a CLEAR CONFIRMATION packet.

Fast Select with data transfer

Here, in Figure 6.5, the user will generate a CALL REQUEST with the facility field coded thus:

Bits:	8	7	6	5	4	3	2	1
Value:	1	0	0	0	0	0	0	0

Once again the user data fields in the CALL REQUEST packet can contain up to 128 octets of user data. Upon receipt the distant Terminal (DTE) could

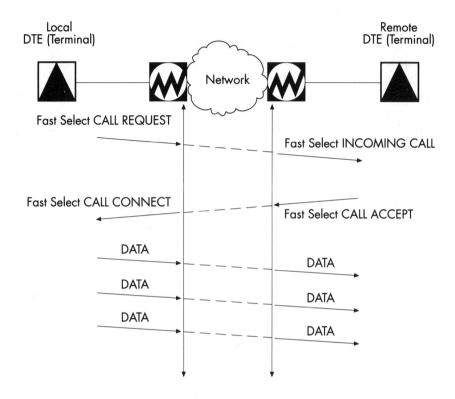

Figure 6.5 Fast Select with data transfer.

issue a CLEAR REQUEST packet containing up to 128 octets of user data. Alternatively, it could accept the call with a packet containing up to 128 octets of data, and then continue with normal communications.

The final CLEAR REQUEST that is issued to terminate the call may, on some networks, contain up to 128 octets of user data. All networks permit the usual maximum of up to 16 octets of user data within the CLEAR REQUEST packet.

Fast Select acceptance

This could easily have been called 'allow incoming Fast Select calls'. The *Fast Select* facility has already been discussed on page 105. Fast Select acceptance authorizes the DCE (Exchange) to transmit to the DTE (Terminal) incoming calls that are requesting the Fast Select facility.

Incoming calls barred

A DTE (Terminal) may only wish to initiate outgoing calls and not be bothered by incoming calls. This subscription-time facility will therefore bar incoming calls to the particular DTE (Terminal). If the facility is in use, any incoming calls will be cleared before they reach the DTE (Terminal) that has barred incoming calls. Note that this facility applies to *all* the logical channels on a DTE (Terminal)/DCE (Exchange) interface that has selected the facility.

Outgoing calls barred

This is the opposite of the above facility. In this case a DTE (Terminal) may only wish to accept incoming calls. This subscription-time facility will therefore bar outgoing calls from a particular DTE (Terminal). If the facility is in use, any CALL REQUEST packets received from the DTE (Terminal) will be cleared by the DCE (Exchange) with a CLEAR INDICATION packet.

Default throughput classes assignment

A *throughput class* is defined as the number of bits per second that can be transferred on a particular virtual circuit (i.e. the rate of data transmission). The default throughput class will always be applied unless another is specified during call set-up. At subscription time the DTE (Terminal) is given a default throughput class that is derived from the speed of the communications link. This default applies to all logical channels on the particular DTE (Terminal)/DCE (Exchange) interface.

In short, this facility allows the DTE (Terminal) to select a default value for the rate of data throughput on a particular interface.

The throughput class for data coming from the DTE (Terminal) that is being called is indicated in bits 8, 7, 6 and 5. Similarly, the throughput class for data coming from the DTE (Terminal) that is initiating the call is given in bits 4, 3, 2 and 1 (see Table 6.3).

Flow control parameter negotiation

There are two parameters that directly affect the flow of data across a virtual circuit. The first is the *window size*, and the second is the *packet size*. In Chapter 5[3] we learnt that the window size is the maximum number of

Table 6.3 Throughput class assignment showing classes and coding.

Bit:	4	3	2	1	Throughput class (bit/s)
or Bit:	8	7	6	5	
	0	0	0	0	Reserved
	0	0	0	1	Reserved
	0	0	1	0	Reserved
	0	0	1	1	75
	0	1	0	0	150
	0	1	0	1	300
	0	1	1	0	600
	0	1	1	1	1 200
	1	0	0	0	2 400
	1	0	0	1	4 800
	1	0	1	0	9 600
	1	0	1	1	19 200
	1	1	0	0	48 000
	1	1	0	1	Reserved
	1	1	1	0	Reserved
	1	1	1	1	Reserved

unacknowledged packets that may exist in any one call. In this particular section the term 'packet size' refers to the maximum number of octets of data that may be carried in the *user data field*. Increasing the window and packet sizes in any direction on a call will usually increase the overall throughput.

With this facility, the DTE (Terminal) that is making the call may select a particular size of window and packet. If a selection is not made, the default values will be used. These could be set by the network or determined by the use of the two facilities: *non-standard default packet size* and *non-standard default window size*. (These facilities will be looked at later in this section.)

Example of flow control negotiation

In Figure 6.6 the calling DTE (Terminal) has generated a CALL REQUEST with a flow control parameter of: Window=4 and Packet=256. On receiving this information in an INCOMING CALL packet, the called DTE (Terminal) decides (for reasons best known to itself) that it wishes to reduce the window size. It accepts the call with a CALL ACCEPTED packet that is sent back with flow control parameters of Window=2 and Packet=256. If the calling DTE (Terminal) is happy with this arrangement the call will continue in the usual way.

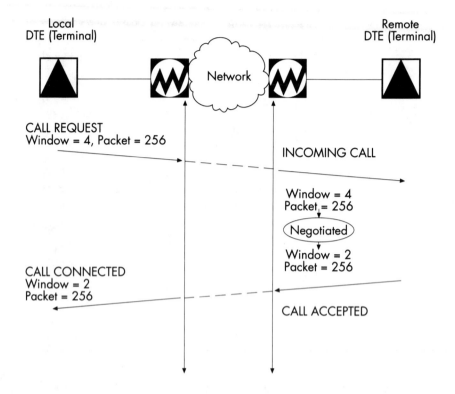

Figure 6.6   An example of flow control parameter negotiation.

Closed user group

In simple terms, the closed user group (CUG) facility allows users of a large, and possibly public, data network to form private groups of users. Access is restricted to members of the same group and functions in a similar way to a club.

In Figure 6.7 we see a simple example of two CUGs: CUG 1 and CUG 2. Within CUG 1 only the three DTEs (Terminals) A, B and C may communicate with one another. CUG 2 consists of DTEs (Terminals) A and D. Note that DTE (Terminal) A can initiate and receive calls from D, but D cannot receive or make calls to B and C.

Closed user group selection

This facility allows the calling DTE (Terminal) to specify a CUG for a particular virtual call. It is an optional facility that is used on a per call basis.

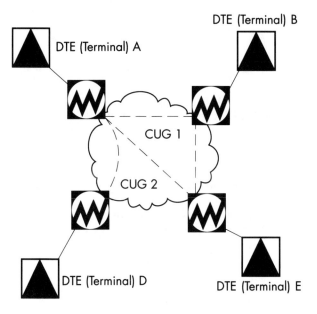

Figure 6.7 Closed user groups.

The request will be contained within the CALL REQUEST packet that originates the call. It may only be requested or received by a DTE (Terminal) if the CUG facility or the CUG with *outgoing access* and/or the CUG with *incoming access* facility has been subscribed to.

The maximum number of closed user groups to which a DTE (Terminal) may belong will be set by the network provider. If the DTE (Terminal) belongs to 100 or fewer CUGs, the basic format of the CUG facility must be used. Between 101 and 10 000 CUGs, the extended format of the facility must be used.

Closed user group access

Closed user group with outgoing access

This facility allows a DTE (Terminal) to be a member of more than one CUG and to initiate calls to DTEs (Terminals) that do not belong to any particular CUG. This facility says 'yes you can have outgoing access' while the CUG with outgoing access selection facility specifies the CUG or DTE (Terminal) that is being called.

Closed user group with outgoing access selection

As said above, the CUG with outgoing access allows the DTE (Terminal) to access other CUGs or DTEs (Terminals) while this facility specifies which CUG or DTE (Terminal) is being called.

Closed user group with incoming access

This is similar to the above, except in this instance a DTE (Terminal) may communicate with other DTEs (Terminals) within the CUG and also receive incoming calls from outside the CUG.

Incoming calls barred within a closed user group

A DTE (Terminal) within a CUG may originate calls within its CUG but not receive calls from other DTEs (Terminals) within the same CUG.

Outgoing calls barred within a closed user group

Here a DTE (Terminal) will be unable to originate calls to other DTEs (Terminals) within its own CUG. It will, however, be able to receive calls from other DTEs (Terminals) within the CUG.

Bilateral closed user group (BCUG)

Another CCITT buzzword that simply means that two DTEs (Terminals) may join together to form their own user group while excluding access to or from DTEs (Terminals) that are not a member of the BCUG. The word 'bilateral' in this sense means 'between the two', rather like two countries that have bilateral talks.

While the BCUG facility allows DTEs (Terminals) to belong to one or more bilateral CUGs, it does not allow calls to DTEs (Terminals) that do not belong to any particular BCUG.

Bilateral closed user group with outgoing access

This allows DTEs (Terminals) to make calls outside a BCUG to DTEs (Terminals) that are not members of any particular BCUG.

Bilateral closed user group selection

This facility is the means by which a DTE (Terminal) can call outside a BCUG to DTEs (Terminals) that are not members of any particular BCUG. It cannot be used unless the bilateral CUG with outgoing access facility has been subscribed to.

On-line facility registration

This subscription-time option was new to the 1984 revision of the X.25 recommendation. It basically allows the DTE (Terminal) either to check the facilities that are in place on a particular interface, or to request new facilities.

On-line facility registration is initiated by the DTE (Terminal) transmitting a REGISTRATION REQUEST packet on channel zero to the DCE (Exchange). The REGISTRATION REQUEST packet shown in Figure 6.8 includes the address fields for uniformity and possible future use. Under current recommendations the address length field is set to zero and the

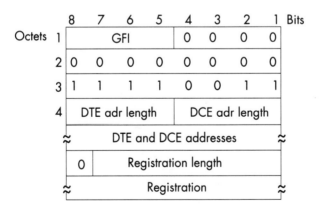

Figure 6.8   Format of REGISTRATION REQUEST packet.

address field is left blank. The registration field may hold up to 109 octets, but should only be present when facilities are to be altered.

Upon receiving the REGISTRATION REQUEST packet the DCE (Exchange) will respond with a REGISTRATION CONFIRMATION packet giving the current state of all the facilities that are currently in force on that particular DTE (Terminal)/DCE (Exchange) interface. The facilities shown in the confirmation packet will remain for all subsequent virtual calls on the interface. It is important to note here that D-bit modification, extended sequence numbering and packet retransmission may only be changed when there are no active virtual calls. The REGISTRATION CONFIRMATION packet also advises of facilities that were not altered, or allowed to be altered, together with the reasons. This information is provided by the use of a suitable cause code, that will now be discussed.

REGISTRATION CONFIRMATION packet

The REGISTRATION CONFIRMATION packet format is shown in Figure 6.9. This packet is transmitted by the DCE (Exchange) to the DTE (Terminal). It provides the current status of an on-line facility request. Within the cause field will be the reason for a facility to be implemented, or an acknowledgement if a request was successful.

The coding of the cause field is shown in Table 6.4.

The diagnostic field is set to zero for a successful registration or will contain additional information in the event of a registration failure.

Under current recommendations the address field will be set to zero.

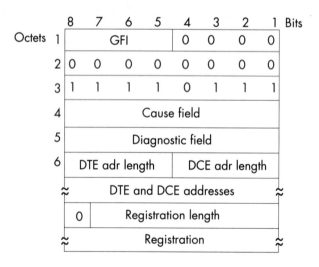

Figure 6.9 Format of REGISTRATION CONFIRMATION packet.

Table 6.4

Bits	8	7	6	5	4	3	2	1
Registration/cancellation confirmed	0	1	1	1	1	1	1	1
Invalid facility request	0	0	0	0	0	0	1	1
Local procedure error	0	0	0	1	0	0	1	1
Network congestion	0	0	0	0	0	1	0	1

The registration field (maximum length, 109 octets) will show the optional facilities that are available, together with those that are currently active on the interface.

Extended packet sequence numbering

This optional facility first appeared in the 1984 revision of the X.25 recommendation. It allows packet sequence numbers to reach a maximum value of 128 rather than the usual 8.[4] The terms modulo 8 and modulo 128 merely mean that packets can be numbered from 0 through 7 (hence modulo 8), and 0 through 127 (modulo 128). Modulo 128 numbering became increasingly necessary with the advent of satellite communications, and the longer transmission delays involved.

Modulo 128 operation requires seven bits for numbering as opposed to three for modulo 8. The packets that contain sequence numbers have therefore had their format changed to accommodate the feature. The packets affected by this are DATA, RECEIVE READY/NOT READY and REJECT.

Figure 6.10 shows two packets, DATA and RECEIVE READY, that have been modified for modulo 128 operation. Here, octet 3 is used for the P(S) number and an additional octet – octet 4 – has been added to accommodate the P(R) number. The M-bit (more data marker) moves from bit 5 of octet 3 to bit 1 of octet 4.

Bit 6 of the GFI (top left field in Figure 6.9) is always set to 1, indicating that modulo 128 operation is in use. Bit 5 will be set to 0.

The RECEIVE READY/NOT READY packets and REJECT packet will have their high order bits in octet 3 set to zero. A seven bit sequence number will then be placed into octet 4.

D-bit modification

The delivery (D-bit) is set to 1 in a data or call set-up packet to indicate that end-to-end acknowledgement is required for packet delivery.[5] Some DTEs

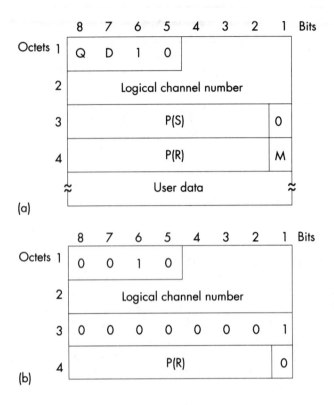

Figure 6.10   (a) DATA and (b) RECEIVE READY packets modified for modulo 128 operation.

(Terminals) may wish to have end-to-end acknowledgement but may not support the D-bit. To overcome this they may subscribe to this facility which will cause the DCE (Exchange) to perform the following.

Packet retransmission

Packet retransmission is an optional facility that is common to all logical channels on a particular DTE (Terminal)/DCE (Exchange) interface. When subscribed to, it allows a DTE (Terminal) to request retransmission of specified packets from the DCE (Exchange).

As an example, by looking at Figure 6.11 we see that the DCE (Exchange) has been happily delivering packets. The last one had a P(R) sequence number of 7. For reasons best known to itself, the DTE (Terminal) decides that it wishes to have packets numbered 6 and 7 retransmitted. It

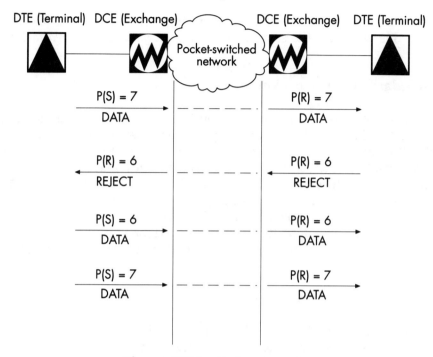

Figure 6.11 Packet retransmission.

will send a REJECT packet to the DCE (Exchange) with a P(R) number equivalent to the first packet that it wishes to have retransmitted; in this case (6). Upon receipt of the REJECT, the DCE (Exchange) will retransmit packet numbers 6 and 7. After this normal transmission may continue.

One-way logical channel incoming

When subscribed to, this facility restricts the use of a specified logical channel (or group of logical channels), to receive only incoming virtual calls. The rules associated with the allocation of logical channels are given in Appendix C. If all the logical channels for virtual calls at one DTE (Terminal)/DCE (Exchange) interface are one-way incoming, this will have the same effect as the *outgoing calls barred* facility.

One-way logical channel outgoing

If this facility is subscribed to, it restricts the use of the logical channel to originating outgoing virtual calls only. If all the logical channels for virtual calls at one DTE (Terminal)/DCE (Exchange) interface are one-way incoming, this will have the same effect as the *incoming calls barred* facility.

Non-standard default packet sizes

The packet size here is the maximum number of octets of user data that may be contained within a DATA packet. All public data networks have a default size of 128 octets. A DTE (Terminal) can use this facility to select a non-standard default packet size. While the actual sizes may vary between networks, typical values are 16, 32, 64, 128, 256, 512 and 1024 octets. Some networks may require that the default packet size must be the same for each direction of data (i.e. for transmission and reception).

Values other than the default may be negotiated for a virtual call using the flow control parameter negotiation facility, mentioned above on page 108.

Non-standard default window sizes

The standard default window size is 2. With this facility, a DTE (Terminal) may select another default in the range of 0 through 7. Some networks may require the default window size to be the same for each direction of data flow.

Values outside the default window sizes may be negotiated for a virtual call using the flow control parameter negotiation facility, mentioned above on page 108.

Reverse-charging

This facility allows 'call-collect' or 'reverse-charge' calls. The calling DTE (Terminal) indicates that it wishes to initiate a reverse-charge call. There is no need to register a similar facility at the DTE (Terminal) that is being called. It merely has to register the *reverse-charge acceptance* facility (see below) with its associated DCE (Exchange). If this facility has not been registered, the distant DCE (Exchange) will CLEAR the call. The top half of Figure 6.12 shows a standard reverse-charge call being made and accepted by the called DTE (Terminal).

Reverse-charging acceptance

Reverse-charging acceptance authorizes the DCE (Exchange) to transmit to the DTE (Terminal) incoming calls that wish to reverse-charge the cost of a

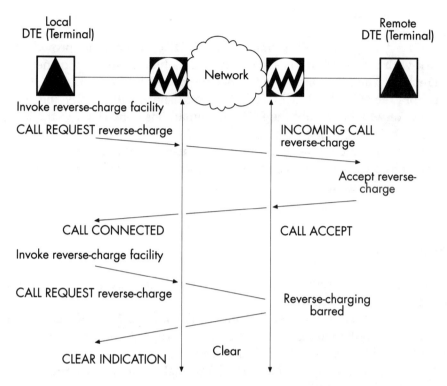

Figure 6.12 Reverse-charging: the top sequence shows the passage of a reverse-charge call. The lower sequence shows a reverse-charge call being rejected by the called DCE (Exchange) because the reverse-charging acceptance facility is not in place.

call. In the absence of the facility, calls will not be allowed. The lower half of Figure 6.12 shows the progress of an unwanted reverse-charge call.

Local-charging prevention

This rather unusual facility prevents the subscribing DTE (Terminal) from incurring any call charges. This is accomplished by various procedural and administrative methods that include the following:

1. Reverse-charging.
2. The identification of another DTE (Terminal) by use of the *network identification facility*. This facility will be looked at next.
3. Not allowing incoming calls that are requesting reverse-charging.

Network-user identification

If subscribed to, this facility enables the DTE (Terminal) to provide the network with information for such purposes as billing, security or network management. The information can either be loaded into a CALL REQUEST packet or the CALL ACCEPTED packet. The facility may be used regardless of whether or not the DTE (Terminal) has subscribed to the local-charging facility mentioned earlier.

It should be noted here that the network user identification information is never transmitted to the DTE (Terminal) that is being called; it is held and only used by the network.

Charging information

This facility is very useful for accounting and costing purposes. It may be invoked on a permanent or per call basis.

On a per call basis, if a DTE (Terminal) is liable for the call charges, the cost of a call may be requested by using an appropriate facility request in a CALL REQUEST or CALL ACCEPTED packet.

On a permanent basis, the DTE (Terminal) will always receive the charging information, without the need to send a facility request in a CALL REQUEST or CALL ACCEPTED packet.

In both cases the charging information is delivered to the DTE (Terminal) that is liable for charges, at the end of a call in a CLEAR INDICATION or CLEAR CONFIRMATION packet.

Hunt group

The hunt group facility was new to the 1984 version of X.25. In simple terms it allows incoming calls to 'hunt' or 'find' a free port on a computer that is presenting itself as a DTE (Terminal). A simple example is shown in Figure 6.13 where four DTEs (Terminals) have addresses A, B, C and D. They all belong to hunt group X. Let us assume that there was an incoming call for address 'X' and that this has been accepted by DTE (Terminal) D.

When the call is accepted by a DTE (Terminal) within a hunt group the address of that DTE (Terminal) will be sent back to the calling DTE (Terminal) in a CALL ACCEPTED packet that is delivered as a CALL

CONNECTED packet. In the example shown in Figure 6.13, the CALL CONNECTED packet will indicate that the call was eventually received by DTE (Terminal) D.

Call redirection

This useful facility first appeared in the 1984 revision of X.25. If a called DTE (Terminal) is busy or out of order, the call may be redirected to another DTE (Terminal). Some networks will only redirect for the 'out of order' condition. It is important to remember that calls may only be redirected within the network of the DTE (Terminal) that generated the original call, and cannot therefore be redirected outside the originating network.

In its simplest form, only one call redirection may be made, but some

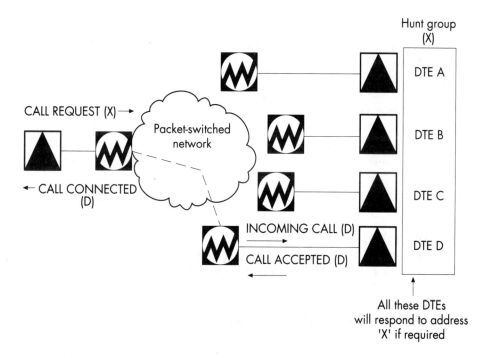

Figure 6.13 Hunt group operation: all the DTEs (Terminals) are in the same *hunt group*. A, B and C are busy and the incoming call is therefore sent to DTE (Terminal) D. Note that the address of the DTE (Terminal) that accepted the call is sent back in the CALL ACCEPTED packet.

networks may offer systematic call redirection, list redirection and logical redirection chaining. Systematic redirection allows the user to determine, in consultation with the network provider, conditions under which calls may be redirected. A good example here would be when a user specifies that he or she wishes to have calls redirected at a certain close of business time (e.g. 1800 hrs). List redirection allows a list of alternative addresses to be stored on the network that will be tried when a call requires redirection. Logical chaining simply means that the call will be redirected through a logical sequence of addresses, e.g. if 'A' is out of order the network might try addresses B, C, D and E, etc.

Whatever happens, the networks will ensure that calls do not end up in a loop and will be careful to ensure that the call does not end up back at the originating DTE (Terminal). The time taken for the call establishment phase will be constrained by the limit set by the calling DTE (Terminal) in Timer T21.[6]

When a call is redirected, some networks will advise the alternative DTE (Terminal) that the call was directed and state the reason, together with the address of the DTE (Terminal) from which the call was redirected. This is achieved by the use of the *call redirection notification* facility that will be looked at next.

Call redirection notification

We saw above in call redirection that it is possible to provide the DTE (Terminal) that eventually receives a call with the reasons for the call being redirected.

The following reasons may be given in the INCOMING packet if the facility has been invoked:

1. Originally called DTE (Terminal) being out of order.
2. Originally called DTE (Terminal) being busy.
3. Request from calling DTE (Terminal) for systematic call redirection.

Called line address modified notification

This optional facility is used by the DCE (Exchange) to tell the DTE (Terminal) why the *called address* in a CALL CONNECTED or CALL INDICATION packet differs from the address that was specified in the original CALL REQUEST packet.

Remember that a CALL REQUEST packet holds the address that it is calling. The destination that it eventually arrives at may have, for example, a different address because of call redirection.

Transit delay selection and indication

In simple terms, transit delay is the amount of time it takes to send a packet through a network. It is an inherent characteristic of a virtual call or PVC and is common to both directions of transmission. The value for transit delay is defined in X.135 and is expressed in terms of a 95 per cent probability value.

Transit delay selection and indication is an optional facility that may be requested on a per call basis. The transit delay value (provisionally expressed in milliseconds) for a particular call will be placed in the CALL REQUEST packet that is used to set up the call. The network, when able to do so, should allocate resources and route the virtual call in such a way that the transit delay for the call does not exceed the transit delay that has been requested.

Questions

1. What is a 'facility' in X.25 terms?

2. Name two instances when a facility may be assigned.

3. Name the four classes of facilities.

4. At what level is the 'facility request' sent?

5. In the facility code field, how many different classes are there and what is the maximum number of facilities allowed in each class?

6. What would be the normal response from a facility request that was denied by the 'called party'?

7. How much user data can a 'Fast Select' with DATA TRANSFER packet normally hold?

8. 'CUG' is an abbreviation for which term?

9. What are the smallest and largest numbers of octets permitted in the user data field of a 'DATA packet'?

10. Give an example of why Modulo 128 would be used in preference to the normal Modulo 8 packet sequence numbering?

11. What is a 'hunt group'?

Notes

1. CCITT Recommendation X.2.
2. For revision of this subject see Chapter 5, p. 69.
3. For revision of the terms 'window size' and 'data packet size' see Chapter 5, p. 85.
4. For more information about packet sequence numbers see Chapter 5, pp. 83–85.
5. For details of the D-bit see Chapter 5, p. 82.
6. For details of T21 and other timers see Table 5.5 on p. 97.

Chapter 7

The 'Triple X' standards

The Triple X standards are the CCITT recommendations numbered X.3, X.28 and X.29. They all refer to the use of PADs (Packet Assemblers/ Disassemblers), a subject that will now be explained.

Packet assemblers/disassemblers

So far in this book it has always been assumed that a user has a DTE (Terminal) that is capable of loading (and unloading) data into packets and performing all the functions required to send and receive packets across the X.25 interface. Figure 7.1 typifies this simple scenario.

Character terminals

Most readers of this book will at some time or another have come across simple computer terminals that have no local intelligence and are often called 'dumb' terminals. For the purposes of this book they will be referred to as *character terminals* because they basically transmit and receive one character at a time. In the real world, situations will frequently be

Figure 7.1 The simple network diagram used in this book which has always assumed that the DTE (Terminal) is capable of working in the packet mode.

125

encountered where one of these character terminals will be able to access a packet-switched network using a type of protocol converter called a *packet assembler/disassembler*, or *PAD* for short. Data are entered into a PAD one character at a time from the dumb terminal and despatched on the X.25 side in packet form.

In Figure 7.2 we see the situation where a character terminal is able to access a packet-switched network using the PAD as an access medium. In this illustration the character terminal is transmitting the message 'The quick brown fox . . .' to the PAD. The PAD will assemble the individual characters into a packet before transmitting it across the X.25 interface. This PAD will also receive data in packets from the distant end and disassemble each packet into individual characters before transmitting them to the character terminal.

It is possible to buy PADs that only serve one character terminal, although the smaller PADs will usually have 4, 8, 16 or even more terminal connections available that share the same X.25 communication link. This situation is shown in Figure 7.3 where eight terminals are using the same PAD. In this instance the PAD is serving eight dumb terminals simultaneously.

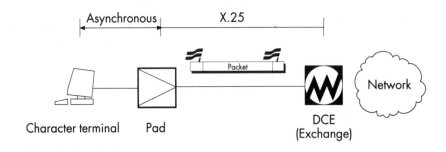

Figure 7.2   A *character* terminal can access a packet-switched network by using a packet assembler/disassembler as a protocol converter.

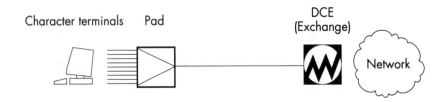

Figure 7.3   PADs will usually support several dumb terminals, using multiplexing techniques to allow the terminals to share the same X.25 interface.

Packet assembler/disassembler architecture

It is important to realize that a PAD does not have to be a specific component such as a box filled with electronic components. It could easily be a communications computer that is *presenting* itself as a PAD. A good example of this is produced by the Tandem Computer Corporation. A Tandem 'midi-computer' can be connected to the X.25 interface and will run a program called *X.3 PAD* to provide all the functions required to comply with the CCITT recommendations that will shortly be discussed.

On the other hand, it is possible to buy PADs in the form of small 'stand-alone' boxes that will act in the same way as a conventional protocol converter. These small 'stand-alone' PADs are a classic example of the progress that has been made in recent years with respect to the miniaturization and cost reduction of computer components. These PADs are computers in their own right, having a microprocessor, memory and peripheral chips to handle the X.25 and character terminal interfaces.

Dial-up packet assembler/disassembler

In Figure 7.4 we see a situation that is frequently encountered on public packet-switched networks. Here a user does not have a dedicated PAD but accesses the network via a modem that in turn calls a modem that is connected to a PAD on the network. This service is particularly useful for users who are travelling and could use a portable computer to access the network.

At this stage it would be worth mentioning that a character terminal could be a personal computer operating in terminal mode or even a large computer system that is presenting itself in terminal mode.

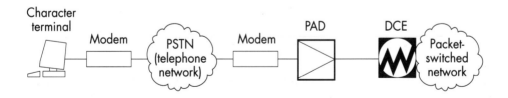

Figure 7.4 Dial-up access to a network. This service is frequently found on public packet-switched networks.

Why use packet assemblers/disassemblers?

At this point we could ask why we should go to all this trouble. If you have read the previous six chapters of this book you will have gained an understanding and appreciation of the benefits of a packet-switching network coupled with the X.25 recommendations that virtually guarantee error-free communication using a wide range of media, e.g. satellites, microwave, fibre optic and telephone cables. A PAD gives a user low cost access into this sophisticated network, by using inexpensive terminal equipment.

We have now seen that a PAD is responsible for the following:

1. Establishing a link with the packet-switched network.
2. Maintaining the link.
3. Assembling and disassembling packets.
4. Communicating with the character terminal.
5. Handling special control processes for the character terminal. (These will be discussed later, but include such items as flow control.)

Packet assembler/disassembler standards: 'Triple X' and 'IA5'

Before discussing the CCITT standards it should be realized that any characters transmitted and received by the PAD must conform to the *International Alphabet Number 5*. This is sometimes known as *IA5* or *ASCII*; a 7-bit binary code to which a parity bit is added.

Nothing can be done in the communications world without having a standard in one form or another. PADs are no exception and here three recommendations are used. The CCITT has been energetic in producing PAD standards. Provisional recommendations were initially published in 1977, followed by the publication of a formal release in 1980. There are three recommendations that affect PADs; these are sometimes known as 'Triple X'. They are X.3, X.28 and X.29. Figure 7.5 shows where these three standards are used.

Recommendation X.3

A PAD does not just act as a crude protocol converter. It also provides some form of additional 'services' to the character terminal. Recommendation X.3 defines the service that is provided to a character terminal by a PAD. These services take the form of parameters that define characteristics specific to the character terminal and its relationship with the PAD. In other words, the

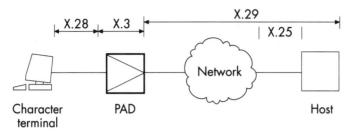

Figure 7.5 Three recommendations are employed when a PAD is connected to a packet-switched network. These are usually known as the *Triple X* recommendations.

value of a parameter will determine the action that a PAD should take when it receives any data from the character terminal.

A good example of the service a PAD offers is given by X.3 parameter 2 which determines whether the character terminal wishes to have its output 'echoed' back to it from the PAD. When keys are struck on a terminal's keyboard, a character will also appear on the terminal's screen.[1] This echo may be generated locally within the terminal (sometimes called *local echo*), or echoed back from the device that the data are being sent to. It is therefore important to determine how echo is used with a PAD. If, for example, your terminal was using local echo and the PAD was also echoing you would end with double characters on your screen (e.g. LLiikkee iitt iiss hheerree)!

This parameter may be changed by the user typing in the following at the character terminal and transmitting it to the PAD. This would normally take place at the beginning of a call between the PAD and the terminal:

To have echo 'ON'   the user would transmit 'SET 2:1'.
To have echo 'OFF'   the user would transmit 'SET 2:0'.

Parameter values

At the time of writing there were twenty-two PAD parameters. These are shown in Table 7.1. These parameters are stored in tables within the PAD and will be accessed to construct a table of parameters to produce a profile that may be associated with a particular port on a PAD. One profile may be used for access to an electronic mail system, while another may be used for direct access to a company's main computer system. The profile may therefore be tailored to suit particular applications. Parameter values may be changed in several different ways. They may be determined by the network or set by the user at subscription time. Alternatively, they can be changed by the host computer when a call from a PAD is initiated or by the user of the character terminal while the call is being set up.

Table 7.1   X.3 PAD parameters.

---

 1. PAD recall
 2. Echo
 3. Data-forwarding characters
 4. Idle timer
 5. PAD to terminal flow control
 6. Suppression of PAD service signals
 7. Action on receipt of Break signal from character terminal
 8. Discard output
 9. Padding after [carriage return]
10. Line-folding
11. Binary speed
12. Flow control of the PAD by the character terminal
13. Line-feed insertion after [carriage return]
14. Padding after [line-feed]
15. Editing
16. Character delete character (IA5)
17. Buffer delete character (IA5)
18. Line display character (IA5)
19. Editing PAD service signals
20. Echo mask of character(s)
21. Parity treatment
22. Page wait

Packet assembler/disassembler parameters in detail

Note that most PAD manufacturers make their own enhancements to the X.3 recommendation. For this reason details of some parameter settings have not been given here.

1. Pad recall

This enables an escape to PAD command state on receipt of specific character.

The transmission of a particular IA5 character by the character terminal will cause the PAD to return to the command state where it will await commands from the character terminal. A typical application would be where a character terminal wanted to have the ability to clear a call with a distant user. The default character is [CTRL + P] which will return the PAD to 'command' state. The user may now enter a new command such as CLEAR or RESET.

An alternative character to [CTRL+P] may be transmitted in the IA5 code range of 2 through 127. The usual default here would be to have a value of (0).

2. *Echo*

Echoing was discussed earlier. This parameter will be set to 0 for echo and 1 for non-echo. It is one of the most frequently used parameters and is handy for applications such as suppressing the text when a user is typing in his or her name and password when accessing a computer system (i.e. overcoming the problem of other people being able to see a user's security codes).

3. *Data-forwarding characters*

It should be remembered that a PAD does not usually transmit one character at a time. It prefers to transmit large chunks of data such as a complete line of text. A typical character that is used for this parameter is [Carriage Return], as this is usually used by a character terminal to denote the end of a line of text. A PAD manufacturer's manual will usually have a table showing options which allow forwarding on (a) every character, (b) any control character, or (c) forward after *n* characters. Alternatively, if the parameter is set to [0] there will not be any particular forwarding character and the PAD will forward data at a time interval set by the *idle timer*, which is the next parameter to be discussed.

4. *Idle timer*

This allows the PAD to buffer for a preset period of time. When set to [0] the idle timer is disabled. Alternatively, any value between 1 and 255 in units of 0.05 seconds may be used. For maximum efficiency it may be desirable to use the highest value, although this will slow down the PAD's response times when working with fast software on the distant machine. A typical value could be 10 which will cause the PAD to buffer data for up to half a second.

5. *PAD to terminal flow control*

If the PAD has an intelligent terminal attached (such as a personal computer transmitting data straight from disk), it is possible that the data will be received faster than the PAD can process and forward it. Parameter 5 gets around this problem by allowing the use of *flow control characters*. If the PAD is being 'over-run' it can transmit a 'Please stop transmission' character to the intelligent terminal, followed by a 'Please resume' when it has cleared the backlog. The two characters [DC1 – X-ON] and [DC3 – X-OFF] are usually used here. Alternatively, the PAD can be set to the familiar 'ENQ'/ 'ACK' sequence. It may also use control signals such as 'CTS'.

6. Suppression of PAD service signals

This stops the PAD sending service signals back to the character terminal in response to events such as the X.25 call being cleared or reset.

7. Action on receipt of break signal from character terminal

The break action referred to here is the sequence, defined for a particular PAD, which is used by the host that the PAD is connected to for indicating that attention is required. This may be used to interrupt a long transmission that the host may be considered to be 'hung in a loop', i.e. stuck in constant transmit mode. With the standard PAD offered by British Telecom's PSS this break will consist of the link being held in the space condition for more than 100 ms. The action of the PAD to this break condition will be one of those selected from the parameter list. For example, if the value is set to [8] the PAD will escape to command mode and await commands from the character terminal.

8. Discard output

When set to [0], data will be delivered to the character terminal in the normal manner. Set to [1] the PAD will discard any data destined for the character terminal. Note that this parameter cannot be set to [1] by an X.29 packet (see below for X.29), nor may it be set to [1] by the character terminal.

9. Padding after carriage return

This parameter allows for the insertion of *padding characters* (character [NUL]), after a carriage return character is transmitted to the character terminal. This effectively creates a delay that allows some of the older mechanical devices such as *teletypes* (teleprinters), sufficient time to move their heads back to the beginning of a line before data transmission is resumed.

10. Line folding

This allows for the formatting of data into regular line lengths when it is delivered to the character terminal. The latter may only have a sixty column wide display, while the data being transmitted to it may have been prepared on an eighty column screen. The value set in line folding (e.g. here 60) will determine the number of characters to be transmitted before a [Carriage Return] is sent to end the line.

11. *Binary speed (Baud rate)*

This is a *read only* value which merely indicates the speed at which the character terminal is communicating with the PAD. The CCITT lays down many values for possible terminal speeds. A good example here is the value [3] which equates to 1200 baud.

Remember that this is an indicator only; it is not used to set the transmission speed between the PAD and the character terminal.

12. *Flow control of the PAD by the character terminal*

This is basically the reverse of parameter 5. This time we are allowing the character terminal to control the rate at which data are sent to it by the PAD.

13. *Line feed insertion after carriage return*

This parameter allows for the numerous different types of terminals that will be encountered in the field. Several values are available to produce the most suitable effect on a user's character terminal.

14. *Padding after line feed*

This operates exactly as parameter 9 except that padding (NUL) characters are inserted after a [Line Feed] has been transmitted rather than the [Carriage Return] in parameter 9.

15. *Editing*

When set to [1] this parameter allows the character terminal to edit characters that are held in a buffer in the PAD and awaiting transmission. The characters that may be used for editing are defined in parameters 16, 17 and 18.

16. *Character delete character (ASCII/IA5)*

Any ASCII character between 1 and 127 may be used except [NUL]. For example, when set to [8] the ASCII [Backspace] character will be used. Parameter 15 must be set to [1] before this parameter is effective.

17. *Buffer delete character (ASCII/IA5)*

As with parameter 16 this is the ASCII character that will cause the PAD to discard the entire buffer of data as generated by the character terminal so far. This is sometimes called the 'line delete character', as a buffer in the PAD will normally only hold one line's worth of user data. A typical value here would be the ASCII code [24] which is the [Cancel] character. This is usually generated by typing [Control + X] at the character terminal keyboard.

18. *Line display character (ASCII/IA5)*

This allows the complete contents of the PAD's buffer to be displayed on a new line on the character terminal. This may be useful to display the state of the buffer after many [Delete] operations have been undertaken. As with parameters 16 and 17, parameter 15 must be enabled before this parameter is effective. Any ASCII character (except [NUL]) between 1 and 127 may be used, but typically the ASCII character [DC2] is used. This is generated by striking the [CONTROL + R] keys on the character terminal.

19. *Editing PAD service signals*

This parameter is used to define the effect of editing buffered characters with the character delete and buffer delete functions.

20. *Echo mask of character(s)*

If parameter 2 is set to 1 (i.e. echo is 'ON'), this parameter will give some control over the selection of the characters that are echoed.

21. *Parity treatment*

This determines whether parity-checking generation is to be invoked. The generation of parity checking is usually considered to be of little value. Under normal circumstances this parameter is best left in the 'OFF' condition.

22. *Page wait*

This effectively allows for pagination of data sent to a terminal. In other words, if a terminal can display twenty-two lines, and the page wait parameter is set at twenty-two, the PAD will send twenty-two lines of data and stop transmission. The PAD will wait until it receives any character from the terminal, whereupon it will deliver another twenty-two lines of data.

Recommendation X.28

Recommendation X.28 defines the procedures used by a character terminal to access the services of a PAD that is (in theory) attached to a public data network. It defines the control procedures used to establish the physical connection to the PAD, the commands that the user sends to the PAD and the service signals sent by the PAD to the terminal user. When a user is accessing a PAD via a telephone network as in Figure 7.4, the X.28 protocol requires that a network user identification (NUI) code is entered by the user. This is purely for billing and accounting purposes.

The physical connection

In Figure 7.6 we see that X.28 specifies V.24 and V.28 (RS–232) for 'dial-up' and X.20[2] if a leased line exists between the character terminal and

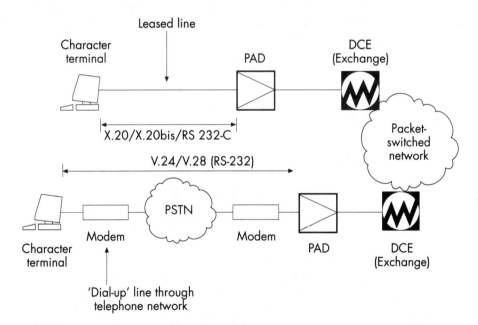

Figure 7.6 The recommendations for X.28 differentiates between leased line access (top), and 'dial-up' access using a modem (bottom).

the PAD. X.28 also defines the protocol that is used for the exchange of characters between the character terminal and the PAD.

Interface states

There are three main conditions (or *states*) that may exist between a PAD and a character terminal. These are *PAD waiting*, *data transfer* and *waiting for command*.

PAD waiting

In this condition the physical connection between the PAD and the character terminal is established and the PAD awaits some call set-up information from the terminal. In this condition, and before any call set-up information is transferred, the terminal may set-up and/or read the PAD parameters. (These were discussed on pages 130–5.) The PAD will revert to this state when a call is complete and cleared, assuming, of course, that the physical connection between the two devices still remains.

Data transfer

In this case a virtual circuit has been established between the PAD and the character terminal. In this condition the PAD is usually invisible to both the character terminal and the distant user that is being called.

Waiting for command

This state is only accessible from the data transfer state. It is entered so that the character terminal can either alter the PAD parameter settings or clear the call.

Packet assembler/disassembler commands and service signals

We have seen that it is possible for a character terminal to issue commands to a PAD to perform such functions as setting up PAD parameters or clearing a call; these commands are called X.28 commands. The 1984 X.28 recommendation allowed for eight PAD commands, although it should be noted that some equipment suppliers will provide *extended* commands that are usually designed to make the PAD easier to use.

Service signals are provided by the PAD to provide the character terminal with status information. One example of a common service signal is 'OCC' which tells the character terminal is OCCupied, or busy. These service signals will be looked at later in this chapter. Meanwhile we will take a closer look at the X.28 commands.

X.28 commands

The eight X.28 commands are as follows:

1. STAT.
2. CLR.
3. PAR?
4. SET.
5. SET?
6. PROF.
7. RESET.
8. INT.

1. STAT

STAT requests status information about the virtual circuit that is currently in use.

2. CLR

CLR will clear the virtual circuit that is currently in use.

3. PAR?

PAR? is short for 'parameters?', and will cause the PAD to list all the PAD parameters.

4. SET

The command SET will amend the PAD parameters. For example the command SET 2:1 changes parameter 2 to 1, thereby enabling 'local echo'.

5. SET?

This is the same as SET except that the PAD will list the PAD parameters after the SET command has been accepted.

6. PROF

PROF is short for 'profile' and allows the user to implement one of twenty-two predetermined parameter profiles that are held in the PAD. For example: PROF 1 will ask for profile 1 to be used.

7. RESET

RESET will reset the current virtual call.

8. INT

INT causes the PAD to transmit an INTERRUPT packet.

Service signals

These service signals are sometimes called *X.28 responses*. They are responses in the form of codes that pass status information back to the character terminal from the PAD.

Recommendation X.29

Normal operation

It will be recalled that recommendation X.3 allows a character terminal to control and set up an associated PAD. X.29 performs a similar function except now the control path is between a PAD and a distant DTE (Terminal). This distant DTE (Terminal) could be another PAD, a host computer or an ordinary packet terminal (see Figure 7.7). By using a PAD as a surrogate, a character terminal may also set up a distant DTE (Terminal); this is one of the most common applications.

As the DTE (Terminal) or PAD uses X.25 as a network interface protocol, all procedures relating to call set-up, call clearing, reset and data exchange follow the X.25 procedures and packet formats. The information necessary for the PAD to perform its function is imbedded in the user data field of packets. This is illustrated for the CALL REQUEST packet in Figure 7.8.

The call user data field of the CALL REQUEST packet may have a maximum of sixteen octets. For PAD operation this is sub-divided into two fields. The first four octets are called the *protocol identifier field*.

The two high order bits of the first octet are coded to indicate a protocol assigned by:

The CCITT	(00)
A national body	(01)
An international body	(02)
DTE (Terminal) to DTE (Terminal) use	(03)

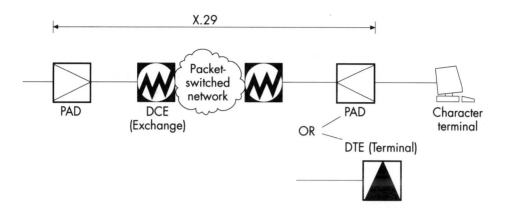

Figure 7.7 Recommendation X.29 details the procedures for the exchange of control information and user data between a PAD and a distant DTE (Terminal). This could be a host computer, a PAD or an ordinary DTE (Terminal).

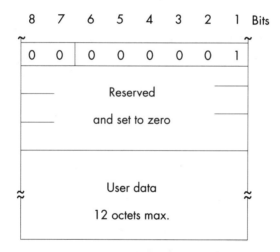

Figure 7.8 X.29 information is imbedded within the user data field of packets. In this example, a CALL REQUEST packet has been shown as an example.

The last six bits of this octet identify the protocol. The remaining three octets are reserved and will always be set to zero. It is anticipated that these three octets will eventually be used to provide additional information about the user who is generating the call.

PAD to PAD operation

The 1980 revision of X.29 allowed PADs to inter-operate directly without the use of an intervening DTE (Terminal), i.e. a packet mode device. The facilities offered by this kind of service are not defined, and it is assumed that the procedures and formats of X.29 would be used, but it is also recognized that other procedures and formats could be applied. PAD to PAD operation would appear to work best with predefined profiles.

Questions

1. What does the abbreviation 'PAD' denote?

2. Explain the difference between 'packet terminal' and 'character terminal'.

3. List the five main functions of a PAD.

4. What are the three CCITT recommendations that are collectively called 'Triple X'?

5. How many PAD parameter values are there (as per 1984 revision X.25/X.3 standards)?

6. What is known about 'parameter 2'?

7. What are the three main 'states' of the interface between the PAD and the character terminal?

8. How many X.28 commands are specified?

9. What is the significant difference between X.29 and the other 'Triple X' standards?

10. Name a recognized 'character set' that is used by PADs and terminals.

Notes

1. For simplicity it is assumed here that we are using a character terminal that has a keyboard and screen. It could, however, have a keyboard and paper output, or indeed be any device that is capable of producing characters in the IA5 format that will be recognized by the PAD.
2. X.29 is the DTE (Terminal) to DCE (Exchange) interface for asynchronous transmission on public data networks. X.20bis is for asynchronous duplex V-series modems.

Chapter 8

Network design

What is a network?

In Figure 8.1 some personal computers (PCs) are shown being used in a variety of ways. At the top of the page is a 'stand-alone' machine that is working purely on its own and is not connected to any other PCs. In the middle are four PCs that are interconnected and sharing a printer. The constraints of the cabling mean that these machines will usually all be in the same building. This is called a *local area network* (LAN). At the bottom of the illustration in Figure 8.1 we see a PC that is connected into a packet-switched network via a PAD. The PC can communicate with any other machine on a network that may span the world. This larger network is called a *wide area network* (WAN). It is best to think of WANs as being any national or international network, and LANs as being those that are contained within a building. This is not a perfect definition but it is sufficient for the purposes of this chapter. Finally, on the right of Figure 8.1 is a LAN that is connected into a WAN. Note that one of the PCs on the LAN is acting as a *gateway* into the WAN.

Why have networks?

In Chapter 1 we saw that computer networks provide effective communications between users, and allow expensive resources to be shared. In the early days computer communications networks gave many users access to the processing power of large, individual and expensive computers. Later, the computers were interconnected to provide resilience and further resource sharing.[1]

Networks that conform to the ISO's OSI model allow the interconnection of a multitude of different devices. This makes for more efficient use of services and resources. An obvious example here would be the ability of inexpensive terminals to have access to an array of sophisticated network

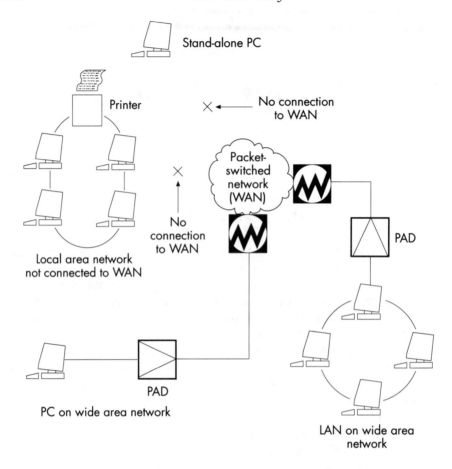

Figure 8.1   Networks: the PC at the top is a 'stand-alone' machine. On the left is a local area network while a single PC at bottom left forms part of a wide area network. On the right is a LAN connected to a WAN via a PC that is called a 'gateway'.

services such as high speed printers and electronic mail. The great advantage of a well designed network is that it is an 'organic' structure that can grow or contract to match the demands made upon it.

Benefits of using packet-switched networks

Listed here are five features that provide the most important benefits of a packet-switched network; these are apart from the most obvious benefits of reliability and error free transmission of data.

1. Integration (of dissimilar systems).
2. Transparent access across networks.
3. Minimal complexity for end user.
4. Purchasing flexibility.
5. Resilience.

These five benefits will now be examined in more detail.

Integration of dissimilar systems

This is an area where X.25 can present network designers with some outstanding benefits. Looking at Figure 8.1, we see a classic example of integration. The PCs on the right of the picture are all connected to a LAN. Let us assume that this network is using IBM's *Token Ring* architecture. Token Ring is totally incompatible with X.25, but by using a gateway[2] the network designer is able to connect a Token Ring LAN to a WAN that in turn allows communication with any other LANs on the network. Similarly, mainframe computers from different vendors may communicate with one another using X.25 as a common interface to the network.[3]

The integration options are almost limitless, as long as computer system vendors are able to supply software that provides an interface complying with the OSI model.

Transparent access across networks

It is now possible for users to communicate between any point on a particular packet-switched network. The use of X.25 and the OSI model allows scenarios where a PC user in London could easily be using an electronic mail system, blissfully unaware that the host computer is actually situated in New York. It is not uncommon for computer systems to be used in a fragmented manner with different applications running on each machine.

Minimal complexity for end user

Packet-switched networks and their associated systems make life easier for the network user. Although some users may continue to access the network through a 'dial-up' link, most will probably be directly connected via a DCE (Exchange) or PAD.

Purchasing flexibility

X.25 has now become such a popular interface standard that there are many vendors competing for the supply of hardware that ranges from massive international networks down to simple four port PADs. For example, let us assume that a company has produced packet switches for many years that supported X.25 trunk speeds of 19.2 kbps. After several successful years they launch a new switch that runs at 64 kbps. The owner of an existing network could upgrade to new technology but use older and slower switches on a new part of the network that does not require such high trunk speeds. Experience shows that redundancy is not usually the norm with X.25-based systems, unlike the normal computer world where users at one time were scrapping systems every few years.

Resilience

Resilience is a key factor when considering X.25 and the design of packet-switched networks. In communications, the term *resilience* is usually used to describe the ability of a network to withstand line and equipment failures. It will be seen later that a packet-switched network should always have an alternative path through which packets may be transmitted in the event of a failure in the main path. Without going into too much detail, take a look at Figure 8.2 where the network consists of three *nodes* made up of three packet switches A, B and C. If there is a line failure between A and B the network could easily route the data via C. This is called *alternative routeing* and is a powerful feature of packet-switched networks. This process requires no intervention from a user who will be unaware that his or her data are being routed through an *alternative path*.

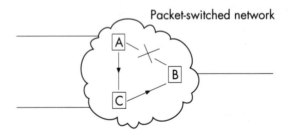

Figure 8.2   Resilience is provided by the ability of a packet-switched network to route data through an *alternative path* if the main path fails. In this example, the main path between A and B has failed; however, the network can still route data via C.

In Chapters 4 and 5 it was seen that the frame and packet levels of X.25 allow for the successful recovery of a communications failure. It is *almost* impossible to lose data on a properly designed network.

Network design: Introduction

The network design process

The network design process, like any other management function within an organization, is the process of allocating scarce resources to solve a business problem. In particular, the network design process is the process of allocating resources within a network to accommodate the demand of the network's users, while still meeting the cost and performance goals set by the organization. The result of this process will be the network design, a description of how the network's resources will be deployed, where equipment will be located and how this equipment will be interconnected.[4]

This may be summarized by a simple illustration (Figure 8.3).

Network resources

These are those resources that are available to handle the demands placed upon the network by the users (either existing or potential). Networks are rarely built from scratch and there are usually elements of an existing system or network in place. For example, an organization may have spare capacity on a mainframe computer to handle some of the new network's administrative function.

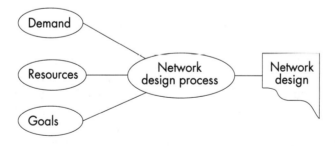

Figure 8.3 The network design process.

The main components or resources of a network are as follows:

1. Lines: these connect the various parts of the network together. An organization may already lease high speed lines that may be used for forming the main trunks on a packet-switched network. Consideration may be given to upgrading existing services to the use of satellites, fibre optics or microwave; these will increase the available bandwidth.

2. Equipment: this is quite simply the hardware that goes to make up the network, comprising the basic network components: terminals, PADs and packet switches.

3. Software: the software or programs that drive the network fall into several main categories:
    (a) communications;
    (b) network management;
    (c) applications (i.e. user software).

Network demand

This is one of the biggest headaches facing the designer – assessing the potential demand. An allowance should always be made for future expansion.

Design goals

These are the criteria that will be used to decide whether a design matches the stated requirements. There will inevitably be some compromise between cost and performance, although this should not be at the expense of providing the users with an acceptable service.

Network resources: lines, packet switches and PADs

There are few drawbacks to using a packet-switched network. The two most critical are (a) the cost of providing error-free transmission and (b) the need to use a protocol such as X.25 to provide a universal interface.

Network designers are unable to dispense with the need for a protocol, but they can address the cost factor by carefully analyzing system requirements to produce the optimum size of switches, PADs and communications links (lines). Many large network vendors have computer models that give an indication of potential requirements.

Lines

Lines are the physical links between the various components on a network. They are also known as circuits, links, trunks and network communications links. Chapter 3 dealt with the standards applied to the use of communications lines.

Analogue or digital lines?

Unless very small networks are being built, it is good practice nowadays to specify 64 or 56 kbps digital circuits for all the trunks on a network. Digital circuits allow for an open-ended up-grade path and remove many of the reliability factors associated with analogue circuits. Analogue circuits are those that purely and simply use basic telephone circuits. The better ones are those that have been certified to work at given transmission rates. Digital circuits have digital transmission throughout and require a 'network termination unit' at the user's premises. It is a good idea to assess the cost of digital circuits on a dollar per kilo-bit basis.

For example, let us assume that the current cost of a 19.2 kbps digital circuit in the United Kingdom is about $12,000. The cost per kilo-bit is

$$\$12,000/19.2 = \$625 \text{ per kilo-bit}$$

The current cost of 64 kbps digital circuit in the United Kingdom is about $28,500. The cost per kilo-bit is

$$\$28,500/64 = \$445 \text{ per kilo-bit}$$

From this it may be seen that in these terms a 64 kbps circuit is about two-thirds the cost of a 19.2 kbps circuit.

Some applications may require higher speeds than 64 kbps. In this case some companies, such as British Telecom, can supply very high speed lines that operate between 2 and 140 Mbps.[6]

Selecting packet switches

Packet switches are key components on any network. If they have insufficient capacity they will create congestion that can easily spread throughout the whole network. Fortunately, manufacturers publish statistical information about their products that will give an indication of the final performance. The word *indication* should be stressed, as each application will drive a switch in a different way.

Switch performance factors

It should be remembered that a delay is incurred every time a packet passes through a switch. This is basically caused by the time taken for the switch to process a packet. Do not forget that a packet does not pass straight through a switch; the supervisory information (such as the address) has to be read and there is a small processing delay caused by the electronics within the switch. The switch also has to contend with the demands of other trunks that may be attached to it.

Vendors will usually equate packet delay in terms of a figure called the *packets per second throughput*. This is the maximum number of packets that a PAD or switch can theoretically handle per second. Another factor that is also relevant to PADs is the speed at which the X.25 link operates. This is sometimes called the *X.25 trunk speed*. Using these two figures, the designer can start to make useful comparisons between different types of equipment.

Another factor that is often quoted by vendors is the *aggregate link rate* (ALR). This should not exceed the sum of the individual trunk rates multiplied by the number of trunks supported. For example: a switch with an ALR of 154 kbps would support 16 trunks: $(16 \times 9600 = 154\,000)$. If the switch only had an ALR of 120 kbps, some of the trunks would have to be run at speeds of less than 9600 bps. Any problems associated with exceeding an ALR will only come to light when all the trunks on a switch start to be fully loaded.

Low performance switches
These are only really suitable for small networks or as a slow speed switch on a part of a major network that does not experience heavy traffic. Typically a low performance switch can handle trunk speeds of up to 9600 bps and support a maximum of sixteen trunks. Packet size may also be limited; a typical maximum size is 256 octets. Another factor to be considered is the maximum number of virtual circuits that may be open at any one time. A figure of fifty may sound impressive but on a switch with sixteen trunks this will mean that each trunk can only support a maximum number of three virtual circuits (when all trunks are active). Finally the packet-switching rate will inevitably be low. Rates below fifty packets per second are fairly typical in this grade of switch.

Medium performance switches
This group will typically support a broader range of interfaces; usually those that allow higher communication speeds. X.21bis, X.21 and V.35 are fairly standard. These switches can often connect directly to high speed digital trunks at speeds of 64 kbps in Europe and 56 kbps outside Europe. Packet-switching rates of up to 500 packets per second are fairly typical coupled with an aggregate link rate of up to 500 kbps. The number of simultaneous virtual circuits that may be open will typically be in a range of between 250 and 1000.

High performance switches
High performance switches will usually be able to support trunks running at speeds of 2 Mbps and have switching rates in the range of 500–2000 (or higher) packets per second.

Selecting packet assemblers/disassemblers

PAD performance factors
PADs may be grouped in the same manner as switches, i.e. low, medium and high performance.

Low performance PADs
These PADs usually have just one microprocessor driving them. Figure 8.4 shows an example of a low performance PAD. This has a minimum configuration of four asynchronous ports and one trunk. The latter has a maximum rate of 9600 bps; the asynchronous ports are restricted to a maximum rate of 9600 bps. An optional expansion board allows for another four asynchronous ports to be supported.

Many of these PADs were designed to provide an X.25 interface for simple, 'dumb', character terminals; a function that they performed

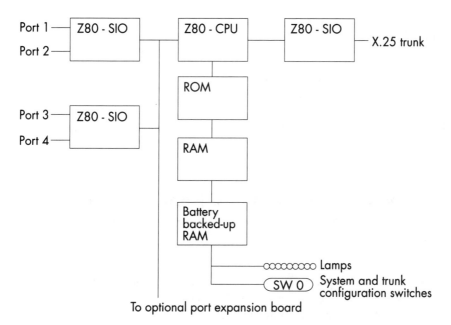

Figure 8.4 Typical architecture of a low performance PAD.

admirably until the advent of personal computers. The character terminals would usually have someone inputting data at a rate that was tied to their typing speeds. With a personal computer, data could be stored on disk or in memory and then pumped in to the PAD at a constant speed of up to 9600 bps. Even with the use of flow control, a sixteen port, low performance PAD would probably have difficulty running sixteen asynchronous ports at 9600 bps continuously. This problem becomes worse when the situation is reversed and a host computer starts to deliver data to the asynchronous ports.

Medium performance PADs
These will usually have a more powerful 16-bit processor. The main characteristics of these PADs is their ability to support trunks at rates up to 64 kbps. The asynchronous ports will support rates up to 19.2 kbps. Packet-switching rates are normally in the range of 50–100 packets per second, based upon 128 octet packet sizes.

High performance PADs
This is a relatively new area and provides considerable scope for development. A throughput of at least a hundred 128-byte packets per second should be a minimum requirement. Trunk rates will be in excess of 64 kbps.

Switching PADs

These are a hybrid device that combine the functions of PADs and switches. A typical model that is currently available will support eight or sixteen X.25 trunks at speeds of up to 19.6 kbps. Sixteen asynchronous ports are supplied, with maximum speeds of 19.6 kbps per port. These switching PADs are ideal for use as concentrators or as major components in the 'backbone' of smaller packet-switched networks.

Design considerations: Network layout

Topology

The *topology* of a network is merely its physical layout and more importantly the way that the major components are interconnected. All networks may be placed under one of the following classifications:

1. Star.
2. Bus.

3. Ring.
4. Tree.
5. Mesh (including heuristic).

Star

The star (Figure 8.5) is a fairly straightforward network configuration. Each major component has a unique link to the central resource. If one link fails, only the users attached to that link would lose network service. This is because there is no alternative or back-up route. The great advantage of this configuration is speed. The connections between the major components and the central resource are direct and do not have to go through any form of switching equipment.

This would not be the type of layout for a packet-switched network, but is often used in LANs. IBM's Token Ring cabling system is a series of interconnected stars.

Bus

The bus layout is rarely (if ever) used for packet-switched networks. It is better suited to LANs and is often found in industrial applications such as robotics. See Figure 8.6.

Ring

The best example of this topology is the Token Ring layout that is used with LANs. It is rarely encountered on wide area packet-switched networks. See Figure 8.7.

Tree

This is a common method of connecting terminals into a packet-switched network, especially when used for an application where the data flow is one-way and outwards from the host system or systems (i.e. 'broadcast'). A simple example here would be a news service that has many printers attached to the network.

The tree is a multilayer design with links between network nodes extending to both the layers above and below. The higher layers (i.e. the three nodes within the cloud in Figure 8.8) may have fast sophisticated switches and high speed communications links between them. Going down the layers one ends up eventually with the printer links in Figure 8.8 that run at a relatively slow speed and are driven from an unsophisticated and inexpensive PAD.

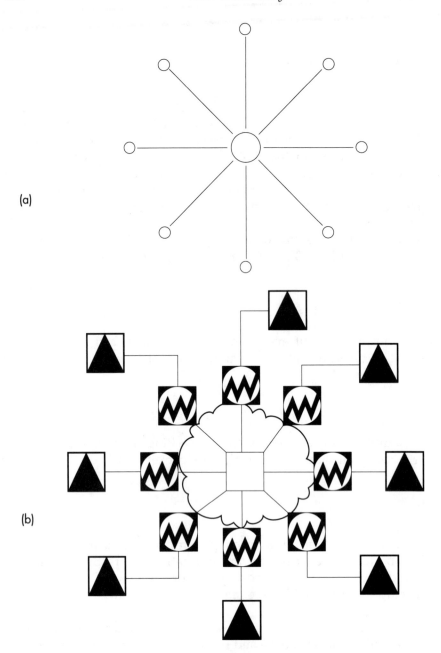

Figure 8.5 Network structure – star: (a) shows the theoretical design, and (b) a practical example. Note that the star is not usually used for packet-switched networks.

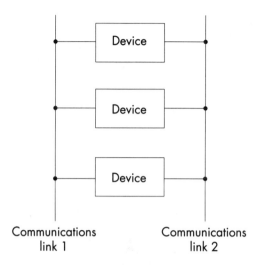

Figure 8.6 Network structure – bus.

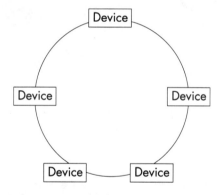

Figure 8.7 Network structure – ring.

Mesh

The mesh topology (Figure 8.9) is probably one of the most common packet-switched network configurations. The basic principle behind mesh networks is that there are always sufficient communications links available. This could be for supporting services when the network is inundated with a high traffic load, or by the re-routeing of traffic when major internodal links have failed. Many packet-switch manufacturers prefer mesh networks because the network management functions are more easily implemented, especially

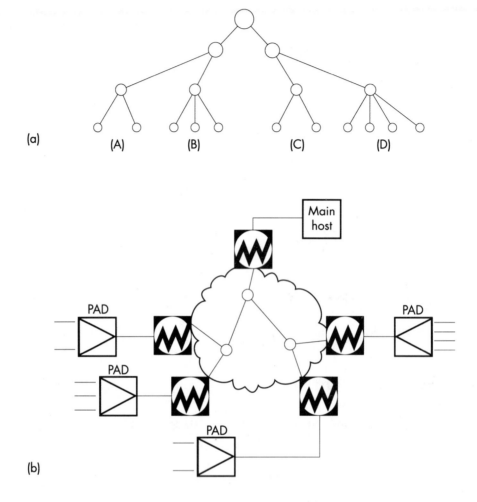

Figure 8.8 Tree network design: (a) shows a theoretical model with the central system at the top; (b) a practical example showing four PADs serving eleven devices.

during disaster recovery. The generation of routeing information is also simplified. Under normal circumstances it would be safe to assume that the packet switches within the main network would normally have the same capacity. On a three link network (i.e. three nodes and three trunks between them) the worst case calculations would usually assume that only one link could fail at any one time.

There are numerous international mesh networks. This is not only because of their resilience but also because it is possible to expand the

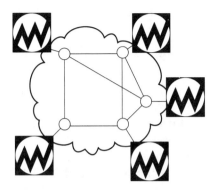

Figure 8.9 Network structure – mesh.

networks easily and quickly, being able to place capacity where it is required. This conveniently leads on to a concept called *heuristic* networks.

Heuristic networks

One dictionary definition of *heuristic* is 'Serving to find out, especially applied to a system of education under which the pupil is trained to find out things for himself'. In this case, the pupil is the network; it is capable of making some decisions for itself. Heuristic networks will assign resources where they are needed most and learn by the decisions they make. This learning cycle can be a slow process. It is usually controlled by a set of parameters laid down by the network designer. The heuristic concept is usually used with mesh networks but could conceivably be applied to tree networks. This would, however, be impractical because of the difficulty in expanding them. Heuristic design sounds impressive, conjuring up images of artificial intelligence and computers that have the power of thought. In reality the whole principle revolves around the clever use of dynamic routeing coupled with some extra network management functions.

The heuristic idea has been around for a long time but has only been made possible by the advent of cheaper microprocessors that may be used in large numbers to provide very powerful packet-switching systems.

This type of network design is nearly ideal, but unfortunately has one notable drawback – cost. To function efficiently these networks require extra capacity, in terms of both packet switches and the high speed links that interconnect them. Heuristic networks, though, are able to provide an almost fault-tolerant system and nearly reach the magical 100% availability figure that network designers strive for.

Network design considerations: Performance

Queuing and queuing theory

An everyday example of a 'queue' would be a line of people who are awaiting their turn to proceed. We need not worry about why they are queuing, it is more important to realize that any queue is serial in form and that its length is dependent upon (a) the number of new people joining, and (b) the speed at which their needs are being satisfied. Queuing theory is merely an attempt to try to design a system that will keep the queue down to the bare minimum without sacrificing efficiency in the process. This may sound fairly simple, but the mathematics behind it are quite involved.

Another way of looking at a queue is in terms of a funnel (Figure 8.10). If the flow is balanced the output rate will match that of the input as in (a). Restrict the outlet, keep the input rate the same and there will be an overflow condition as in (b). Figure 8.10(c) shows the reverse of this situation where the input has been increased, resulting in another overflow

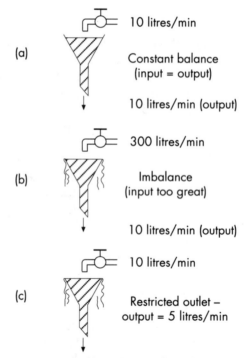

Figure 8.10 Queuing may be likened to the effect of pouring water into a funnel. In (a) the input=output. In (b) there is an overflow because the input is greater than output capacity. In (c) there is an overflow because output capacity is reduced.

condition. This may appear to be rather trivial but it is the basis behind queuing theory in packet-switched networks.

The example in Figure 8.10 shows how important it is to know how much data are going into a switch (the input), how quickly the switch can process the data (the task) and finally how quickly the data may be transmitted away from the switch (the output). Figure 8.11 graphically represents these three criteria.

Looking at a packet switch again we can start to see queuing in more practical terms. Assume for a moment that a switch can process a finite number of packets (the 'task'). This overcomes the problem of processing speed but still leaves further possible complications. The input could be running at a higher speed than the output, thereby causing the switch to start backing off or declining some of the inbound traffic. This sounds fine until we realize that this creates further inbound traffic and increases the task load on the switch as it handles out-of-sequence packets that will be received and subsequently rejected.

Reliability

Mention should be made about the factors affecting reliability. It is often a subject that is taken for granted but has serious implications when dealing with network design. Reliability may be defined as 'a measure of the ability of a product to function successfully, for the period required, in the specified environment'.

Three parameters may be associated with reliability:

1. The equipment and the performance required of it.
2. The conditions under which it will operate.
3. The time interval or duration of operation.

These factors are fairly obvious when stated on paper, but are often

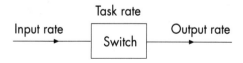

Figure 8.11 The three variables that affect queuing: input rate, processing rate of switch (task) and the output rate.

overlooked when dealing with the purchase of communications hardware. How many times are PADs purchased without reference to the manufacturer's ambient temperature requirements? PADs do not always go into air-conditioned computer rooms; they often end up in a unvented cabinet in a room that is not air-conditioned. It is not widely known that components such as integrated circuits do not fail instantly when run too hot. The component is 'stressed' and the life of the component is reduced. In other words, you can get away with baking hardware today but the long-term reliability is jeopardized.

One good example of reliability in design is the difference between commercial and military specifications. A component used in a tank in the desert will be operating under different conditions from those of one in an air-conditioned computer room. Network designers will often forget this when ordering equipment for tropical and Middle Eastern countries. Communications equipment in some countries will have to tolerate fluctuating mains power, heat and a possible shortage of local expertise to maintain it.

Understanding reliability specifications

One of the most frequently quoted figures in equipment specifications is *mean time between failure* (MTBF). MTBF is a useful figure for communications systems where the equipment is in continuous use. In simple terms it is an indication of the potential reliability of the equipment. It is particularly useful for comparing equipment from different manufacturers. Two vendors may have equipment with similar characteristics but with different MTBF figures. A simple rule of thumb is that the higher the MTBF figure, the more effort has been placed into reliability design. This is often the case with power tools where the 'professional' models will usually have a higher MTBF figure than the 'domestic' models, although they appear to do the same job.

Another useful figure is *mean time to repair* (MTTR). This is an estimation of the average time that it will take to repair a piece of equipment. This has an effect upon the availability or 'up-time' of the system. The time taken to repair a device is only of significance when the MTBF is taken into account:

$$\text{Availability} = [\text{MTBF}/(\text{MTBF}+\text{MTTR})] \times 100$$

The most dramatic effects upon reliability will be made when regular network maintenance is carried out. Error logs on PADs and switches can give an indication of where problems are beginning to occur.

Network design considerations: Security

Security is rapidly becoming one of the biggest problems confronting network designers and operators. Security with respect to packet-switched networks falls into two main areas: (a) prevention of unauthorized access to user data, and (b) preventing unauthorized access to network management functions. The latter is particularly sensitive as an intruder could shut down a complete network if the relevant information was available.

Most networks will provide three basic security features:

1. Network management security.
2. Network administration security.
3. User access security.

Network management security

This allows the operator terminals (those terminals that are used for running and managing the network) to interact directly with the network. These operator terminals will often have security created by being able to work only within a particular closed user group (CUG). This overcomes the problem of rogue terminals being able to access the management function of a network. Each terminal will usually have its own unique identifier and password. This is supplemented with a capability factor that restricts the terminal to predetermined functions. These parameters can be changed and verified by a master operator terminal that will have access to all parts of the network. The actual commands issued by these terminals will be logged by the computer that provides the administrative function. This machine may also provide a display of the operator terminals that are logged on to the system.

Administration system security

This is the computer system that provides all the administrative functions such as accounting and the logging of operator terminal commands. These systems are usually mainframes or large minicomputers with security often being provided by the computer's own access control mechanisms.

User access security

Large international networks frequently have many thousands of users. Physical security may be provided by restricting network access to specific facilities and also by using password protection. Groups of users sharing common facilities may have the protection of CUGs.

Data encryption

Security of a user's data may be provided by *encryption*. The science of encrypting information is called *cryptography*, a subject that is beyond the bounds of this book. A simple example is shown below where the ubiquitous message 'The quick brown fox . . .' has been reversed.

Plain text:

> The quick brown fox jumps over the lazy dog's back

Encrypted:

> kcab s'god yzal eht revo spmuj xof nworb kciuq ehT

This is simple, but can often be sufficient to provide some basic security. This method is known as 'substitution cipher'. Another simple substitution cipher is the 'shifted alphabet' where characters are left- or right-shifted several places. This type of method is also called the 'Caesar Cipher', as is it was used by Julius Caesar.

Plain text:

> The quick brown fox jumps over the lazy dog's back

Alphabet-shifted (one place right)

> Uif rvjdl cspxo gpy kvnqt pwfs uif mbaz eph't cbdl

Network purchase: Alternatives

Alternatives to building your own network

There are many alternatives to building your own network, even if the main requirement is for packet switching. Many companies now offer the use of their own networks and it should not be forgotten that most of the technically advanced countries have national public packet-switched networks that provide international links to other networks. In the United Kingdom British Telecom offer the highly successful *Packet SwitchStream*

(PSS) service. This is a classic example of a network that spans the United Kingdom and provides modern facilities. As a matter of interest it should be noted here that PSS is considered to be one of the best and most exact implementations of X.25.

Other private companies, such as Geisco, Tymnet and Telenet, are able to provide network services. One of the world's largest private packet-switched networks was provided by Tymnet for Telerate, a company that is part of Dow Jones Information Services. Telerate have total control of the network and maintain the Tymnet equipment that is attached to it. Two separate network control centers are located in the USA to provide resilience in the event of a total outage or failure at either site.

General design parameters

Any network design will need to fulfil most of the following requirements:

1. All of the criteria that will shortly be discussed in the section on specific design parameters below.
2. The user's specific requirements.
3. All of the above objectives within a specified time-scale and within specified cost limits.

Specific design parameters

Performance versus cost

As so often happens when talking about the design of a system or product, we end up with the equation of *performance versus cost*. Looking at the basic requirements and considerations one ends with the following criteria.

How many packet switches are required to build the basic 'backbone' network?
This decision is influenced by the number of users who will be accessing the network, together with the distance between them.

How should the switches be connected to one another?
This factor is influenced by the cost of the communications lines together with the speeds at which the lines can operate. Some countries such as the United States and the United Kingdom are able to offer some excellent lines while other, less technically developed, countries offer slow and often unreliable lines.

Remember that the cost of a line is usually proportional to its maximum speed and quality. On some networks speed is essential, while on others it will be a secondary consideration. At this point the designer will have to take a close look at the use that will be made of the network. If it is doing something interactive, e.g. connecting to a database or electronic mail system, speed will be important. On the other hand the network may be used to transfer data in batch mode between systems overnight. In this case time may be of little consequence.

How will users access the network?
The variations here are numerous. Two classic examples are shown in Figure 8.1 where one solitary PC is using a PAD while four others are accessing the network via a gateway that is bridging the two networks.

Which way are the data moving?
This question is not so obvious but is of great importance. It will affect the *topology* (physical layout) of the network, and consequently the positioning of the trunk circuits that interconnect the major components of the network. Data flow could be random, two way or one way. With one way the direction of flow should be determined. Data moving towards a central point on a network could make higher demands on resources than data being distributed outwards.

Time delay
To achieve the minimum transmission times there will need to be a minimum of switching points on the network. Packet networks are fast but there is always some transmission delay.

The normal time delay that may be tolerated for any particular transmission is called the *average delay* time. High speed circuits and sophisticated equipment will reduce this to a minimum. Remember, though, that there is little value in ending up with a racehorse pulling a hay cart. On large networks the main trunks should all be specified as digital circuits. In the United Kingdom these are now running at a maximum speed in the region of 140 Mbps. The use of these digital trunks allows for open-ended expansion. Smaller networks may be able to use less expensive circuits.

Reliability
The terms 'reliability' and 'resilience' are interrelated here. Most packet-switching hardware is physically reliable, but the equipment can suffer from external problems such as mains power failure or even such extremes as flooding. A careful assessment of the resilience required from the network will reveal how much duplication will be required of switching centres and

lines to provide back-up facilities. It is possible to use 'dial-up' (switched telephone line) services, but these will inevitably degrade the service and are not considered to be a choice that is worthy of consideration.

Network purchase: Management

This section will look at some of the commercial aspects of buying a network and the questions that should be asked when confronting network vendors. Many efficiently run organizations do not apply the same criteria to network purchasing as they do to buying services in other parts of the organization.

Appoint a project manager

The first step in any major project is to appoint a project manager. There are numerous reasons for this; the best is probably because he (or she) will provide vendors and users with a single point of contact. This person would ideally have a technical background, but this should not be at the expense of sound management skills. A good overview knowledge of technical issues can often give a project manager a better perspective than someone who may become buried in technical detail and lose sight of the overall requirements.

Specification of requirement

This is a document that simply details the criteria for the network. The document is broken down into several parts.

Define normal operating practice

This section should include some information about how the company or organization works. Corporate 'glossy' literature will give vendors an insight into the character of the organization. Existing communications and computer systems should be detailed, preferably on some form of map that will allow the designer to block structure the network. This map should also include ancillary equipment such as personal computers, telex and fax machines. Put these down even if they are not currently part of any communications system. The important issue here is to evaluate the current situation within the organization.

Identify users

This may sound pretty obvious but it is surprising how often the question is overlooked. There is a danger of only looking at the obvious users, such as those using computer terminals and PCs. One should not forget, however, that there may be many other potential users who would benefit from a terminal when an efficient network has been installed. This is especially true when a value added service, such as electronic mail, is added to the network. Vendors of electronic mail systems are well aware of the sudden increase in demand for terminals that often accompanies the installation of a new system. For example, users of telex and fax machines suddenly realize that there is an easier way to communicate.

The analysis or census of potential users should be broken down into some meaningful grouping. One way of doing this is to group by location and access level requirement. For example, San Francisco may have fifty potential users, thirty-six of whom are using the network for intermittent, low priority access to a computer system in New York. The other fourteen are in the orders department and use their terminals for credit rating assessment, where fast response times are essential.

Define goals

In other words – what need is the network expected to satisfy? This is a vital question for any project manager. It is important to define the requirements clearly, as his or her success will be judged against them. Defining this goal will also enable him or her to overcome some of the inevitable problems that occur on a large project. If, for example, the company states that cost must be minimal, it should not be surprised if a relatively slow and limited network is built. On the other hand, many organizations believe that speed is important; often when there is little demand for it. This corporate attitude is evident in the number of powerful microcomputers that are changed every two years for the latest 'go-fast' model when they are only ever used for word processing.

Integration period

How is the transient phase going to be handled when users switch from the existing systems over to the new network? Apart from the obvious problems there are also the issues of training and documentation to be considered. If at all possible it would be best to test the network with a few users at first and then slowly to load it up over a period of time. This obviates some of the problems that often occur when all users switch on for the first time.

Documentation and progress reviews

The project manager should at all times have control of the project, and the various third parties associated with it. One obvious method is to hold regular design review meetings. These are usually minuted with action points highlighted. The network designer should produce a 'Design Review Document' detailing the rationale behind his design together with data and calculations to support it. At each meeting the designer would be expected to report on progress and discuss any issues that have arisen during this phase. This is an excellent opportunity for the buyers to test the usefulness of network providers that offer a design service. Asking for the review document may meet with excuses about time-scales, but the point should be pressed.

Time-scales

How long is it going to take? Answers such as 'How long is a piece of string?' are not acceptable. Network providers, whether an internal department or an outside company, should be able to give a detailed forecast of the timing of major stages in the project. Some companies investing in a major international network may consider introducing penalty clauses into a contract with the vendor. A 'horizontal' or 'time-line' event planner is of great value here, and overcomes a lot of the problems associated with presenting detailed project information. This planner should have major 'milestones' noted on it. For example: equipment installed date, test date, live date.

Network purchase: Site planning

Site planning

This does not have a direct impact upon network design but is worthy of consideration. The subject can be divided into three main areas:

1. Space requirements.
2. Cabling plan.
3. Environment.

Space requirements

The location of central switching equipment may be dictated by the location of the largest group of users and also by the availability of space for the equipment. Very small switches and PADs can sit on a desk. It is also possible to buy single port PADs that slot into a PC. These effectively act as a gateway or protocol converter. When planning for space remember to make allowances for expansion at a later date. Networks can grow at a staggering rate, especially when newly installed into companies that have not realized the benefits of a sophisticated and reliable network.

Cabling plan

Cabling is one of the hidden costs of network design. The cost of the cable itself is not too much but adding labour charges increases the price dramatically. This is especially true when installation may only be undertaken at weekends or during holiday periods. It may be less expensive to concentrate terminal users into local clusters to reduce cabling costs. Money may also be saved by using existing cables, or using *block wiring systems*. With these, a loom of twisted pair cables is laid throughout the building and ends in a large patch panel.

Environment

On large installations there will almost certainly be a need for a purpose-built computer room with a false floor (to allow air flow and easy cabling) and air-conditioning. Automatic fire extinguishing equipment (ideally a Halon gas system) will be required together with a 'clean' electricity supply. Many stories have been told of intermittently defective computers that turned out to be connected to the same power line as the office lift. The term 'clean' here refers to the absence of electrical interference; often called 'noise'. If a three phase supply has been provided, it is good practice to wire individual equipment cabinets to different phases. This will ensure that the whole communications room does not go down when one phase of a supply is lost.

The contract with the electrical installation company should state that the electricity is 'clean' and conditioned for the type of use that it is being put to.

Battery back-up is often referred to as a UPS (uninterruptible power supply). This is a necessity on most large installations and would ideally be backed up by a motor generator set. Many communications rooms will have the mains supply fed to a UPS and the equipment fed from the batteries of the UPS. This ensures that there is no power interruption when the mains fails. Battery back-up units are usually measured by the number of minutes for which they can supply power during an interruption of mains supply. The cost is massive, however, and can easily match the cost of the communications hardware in some cases.

Network design: An example

This section is intended to give an example of the concepts relating to network design. The emphasis has been placed on showing how the various components are brought together. The detailed side of network design (such as the calculation of loading factors) has not been discussed as the subject is beyond the scope of this book.

Background

A fictitious company has an existing network that is to be upgraded to a packet-switched network. Figure 8.12 shows the network topology in the existing network. Note that the users can only communicate between fixed points. This gives rise to the name of 'point-to-point' for this type of layout. The network topology in London and in New York is a classic example of the 'star' layout that was mentioned on page 151. This international organization has main offices in New York, Tokyo and London. Two large computer centres are located in London and New York, both equipped with mainframe computers. Minicomputers are used in other cities and intelligent use has been made of personal computers. The latter are networked on to IBM Token Ring LANs.

These computer systems are used to access and update a database that is currently replicated in New York and London. The internal systems at each city handle day-to-day administration, with the communications links primarily being used to access and update the database.

The project can be initially approached using the three major criteria that were mentioned earlier in this chapter, namely: network resources, network demands and goals.

Network resources

The organization has some sophisticated computer equipment that will form part of the new network. Two large mainframe computers will become part of the major nodes on the network.

In detail, the organization has the following existing computer systems:

United Kingdom

London
- One mainframe with a hundred character terminals attached.
- Three IBM Token Ring LANs.
- Six synchronous communications ports driving the existing point-to-point lines.

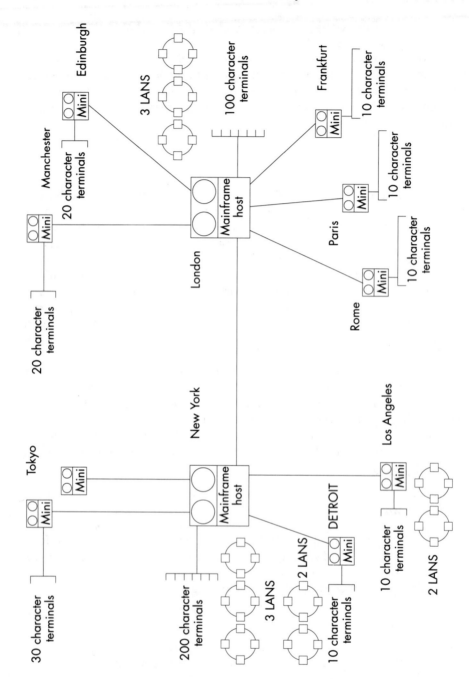

Figure 8.12 Example of network design: the organization's existing 'point-to-point' network.

Manchester
- Mini-computer with twenty character terminals attached.

Edinburgh
- Mini-computer with twenty character terminals attached.

Mainland Europe

Frankfurt, Paris and Rome
- Each centre has one minicomputer with ten terminals attached, together with one IBM Token Ring LAN.

Japan

Tokyo
- Two minicomputers, each with thirty terminals attached.

Americas

- Mainframe with 200 character terminals attached.
- Three IBM Token Ring LANs.

Los Angeles
- One minicomputer.
- Ten character terminals.
- Two IBM Token Ring LANs.

Detroit
- One minicomputer.
- Ten character terminals.
- Two IBM Token Ring LANs.

Network demand

Under normal circumstances a detailed analysis would be made of the requirements for the whole network. As stated earlier, the scope of this book does not extend to providing details of how this process is undertaken. The main aim here is to introduce architectural concepts.

The database is distributed across the two mainframes in New York and London. This database is updated once a day but the organization now wishes to have both parts of the database simultaneously updated as soon as any changes occur. This means that there will be a slow and steady stream of 'peer to peer' (i.e. high level) traffic as the database is updated. It will also generate bursts of data from the minicomputers in each centre. This will also be compounded by the requirement for the LANs to have access to the database.

Goals

1. The distributed database should always be promptly updated.

2. Improved line quality: the organization has experienced problems with the lease analogue lines that currently form the point-to-point network. These have been found to be expensive, unreliable and are now working at their maximum capacity.

3. The new network must provide back-up links and resilience. The company suffered financial losses when the transatlantic link went down for two days in recent months.

4. All computer systems within the organization require fast and accurate access to the database.

5. An efficient network management service is required.

6. Security is important as the organization's management is concerned about 'hackers' and their effect upon the organization's image. The information itself is not particularly sensitive and there is no need for encryption.

7. Any network solution must provide an open-ended upgrade path that excludes any upgrading of the existing computer systems. In the past, money has been spent on new mainframes that ended up becoming expensive communications processors.

The solution

Figure 8.13 shows the proposed topology of the new network. The first item that should be apparent here is the use of the classic 'triangle' between nodes to provide alternative paths in the event of failure of any one trunk. If, for example, the transatlantic trunk fails, a path still exists to New York via

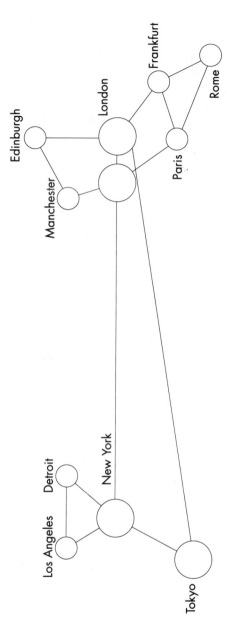

Figure 8.13 Example of network design: proposed 'backbone' of the packet-switched network. Each circle represents a packet switch.

the switch in Tokyo. This meets one design goal which was to provide resilience in the event of communications link failure.

Digital trunks with a speed of 64 kbps will be used throughout Europe. The rest of the world will have 56 kbps digital trunks. These high speed digital trunks are expensive, but provide accuracy and an easy upgrade path. It is pointless to install analogue major trunks. They are inherently unreliable and are unable to provide sufficient *bandwidth*[5] for increasing network capacity.

Each node would only be loaded to a maximum of 50 per cent. This is because there is only one alternative path available for routeing. Figure 8.14 explains this in more detail. The network control centre functions will also load LDN-1 and LDN-2 nodes by an extra 25% (peak).

The major international links would be PVC while all national traffic is SVC. The PVCs on the international trunks save the call set-up time, thereby improving the effective performance of the network.

The Token Ring LANs will at some stage need to update and access the database. Token Ring networks operate with data transfer speeds of 4 Mbps and upwards. If fed directly into the network this could cause network congestion, when confronting the relatively slower network transmission rate of 64 kbps. To overcome this potential problem, the updating of the database will be undertaken by the hosts (i.e. either by a mainframe or by

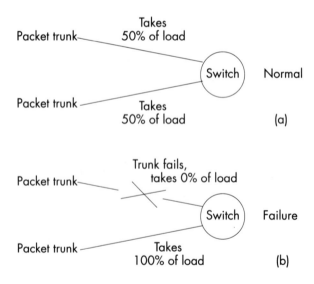

Figure 8.14 (a) Each trunk on this node can only be loaded by 50 per cent. In the event of one trunk failing (b), the other will take 100 per cent load.

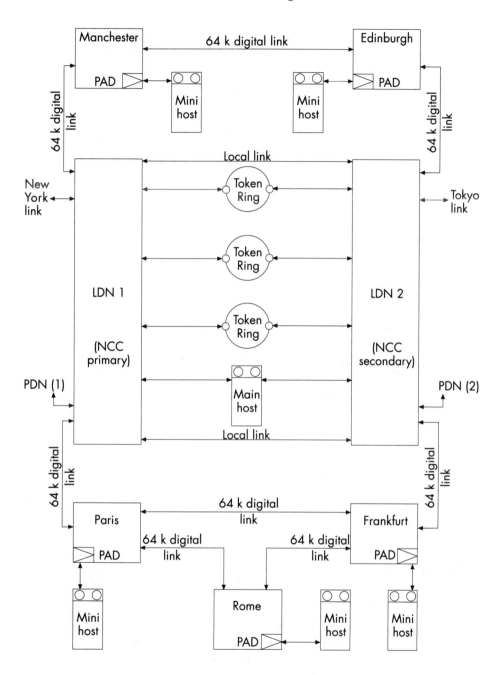

Figure 8.15 Schematic of European part of proposed network.

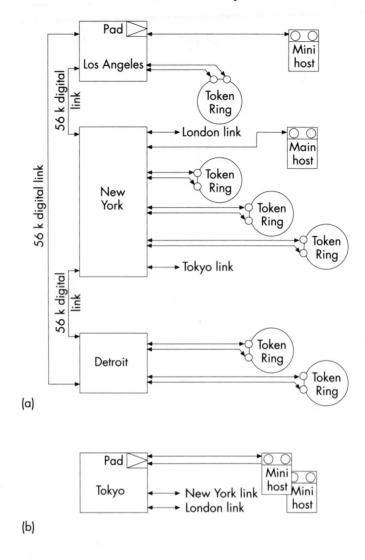

(a)

(b)

Figure 8.16   Schematic of (a) American and (b) Japanese parts of proposed
network.

one of the minicomputers on the network). This is essentially a way of
buffering the burst of data that the LANs could generate.

Each LAN accesses the network via a gateway machine that is a PC with
a plug-in X.25 interface card. The gateway machines in London will have
two of these cards, thereby providing alternative routeing through LDN-1 or
LDN-2.

The connection between the minicomputers and the network is provided via a low performance PAD. This PAD acts as a protocol converter, providing the minicomputer with X.25 access into the packet-switched network. The packet to the switches for the two mainframe computers is provided by a software application that allows the existing synchronous interfaces to be used to present themselves to the switches in X.25 format. This makes good use of the existing hardware on the two mainframes. The remaining unused mainframe ports will be retained for any possible expansion of the network.

The network control centre function will operate in either of the two packet-switching nodes in London (LDN-1) and (LDN-2). All routeing and network management is undertaken from London. This decision takes advantage of the fact that London bridges the time zones of New York and Tokyo. This enables the operators to communicate easily with personnel at these other two nodes.

Figures 8.15 and 8.16 show the network in schematic form.

Security has been addressed and the requirement assessed with reference to the original design goals. The system will operate in such a way that the minicomputers will act as a buffer or 'cache' for the terminals and LANs that wish to access the database. SVCs are used between the minicomputers and the LANs/Terminals, while PVCs are used between the minicomputers and the mainframes where the database is held. This has the advantage that the LANs and terminals only have local access, and no direct access is possible between one of these devices and the main network (see Figure 8.17).

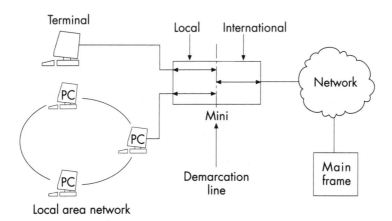

Figure 8.17 The minicomputer here is used as a buffer or cache between the WAN and the local devices, thereby ensuring that they do not have unrestricted access to the WAN.

Questions

1. What is the advantage of a network?

2. What is the difference between a LAN and a WAN?

3. Why is a mesh network more reliable than a point-to-point type network?

4. What is the unique feature of an 'heuristic' type network?

5. What is meant by the abbreviation PSS?

6. What does the term 'Packets per Second Throughput' equate to, and why is it so important?

7. Name two of the easiest ways of providing security on a packet-switched network.

8. Explain the following terms:
   (a) MTBF
   (b) MTTR.

9. Define the word reliability when used in the context of network design.

10. What is meant by the term Aggregate Link Rate?

Notes

1. See Chapter 1, p. 3, for more information on this subject.
2. A 'gateway' is a device that provides a bridge between dissimilar networks. In this instance the bridge is between a Token Ring LAN and the X.25 interface to the packet-switched WAN.
3. It should be noted here that mainframe computer communications tend to polarize around either IBM's Systems Network Architecture (SNA) or X.25. IBM machines can support X.25 but the preferred option is usually SNA. For more information on SNA refer to M. Schwartz, *Telecommunications Networks: Protocols, modeling and analysis*, Addison-Wesley, Reading, Massachusetts, USA, 1987.
4. Extracted from Robert L. Ellis, *Designing Data Networks*, Prentice Hall, Englewood Cliffs, New Jersey, USA, 1986.
5. 'Bandwidth' is a measurement of the signalling space on a communications link or channel. The wider the bandwith, the more data can be transmitted across the link.
6. The costs are quoted here in dollars because of the international market for this book.

Appendix A

Addresses for standards information

CCITT recommendations, including X.25:

The General Secretariat
International Telecommunication Union
Place de Nations
1211 Geneva 20
Switzerland

United States Department of Commerce
National Technical Information Service
5285 Port Royal Road
Springfield, VA 22161
USA

ANSI Standards:

American National Standards Institute, Inc.
1430 Broadway
New York
NY 10018
USA

EIA Standards:

EIA Engineering Department
Standards Sales
2001 Eye Street, NW
Washington DC 20006
USA

British Telecom Packet SwitchStream (PSS):

Packet SwitchStream
National Sales Office
Seal House
1 Swan Lane
London
ED4R 3TH
UK

Telephone: 071–357–4061

British Standards and ISO Standards:

BSI
Linford Wood
Milton Keynes
MK14 6LE
UK

Appendix B

Coding of X.25-generated diagnostic fields

Table B.1 Coding of X.25 network-generated diagnostic fields in CLEAR, RESET and RESTART indication, REGISTRATION CONFIRMATION and DIAGNOSTIC packets.

Diagnostics	Bits								Decimal
	8	7	6	5	4	3	2	1	
No additional information	0	0	0	0	0	0	0	0	0
Invalid P(S)	0	0	0	0	0	0	0	1	1
Invalid (PR)	0	0	0	0	0	0	1	0	2
	0	0	0	0	1	1	1	1	15
Packet type invalid	0	0	0	1	0	0	0	0	16
For state r1	0	0	0	1	0	0	0	1	17
For state r2	0	0	0	1	0	0	1	0	18
For state r3	0	0	0	1	0	0	1	1	19
For state p1	0	0	0	1	0	1	0	0	20
For state p2	0	0	0	1	0	1	0	1	21
For state p3	0	0	0	1	0	1	1	0	22
For state p4	0	0	0	1	0	1	1	1	23
For state p5	0	0	0	1	1	0	0	0	24
For state p6	0	0	0	1	1	0	0	1	25
For state p7	0	0	0	1	1	0	1	0	26
For state d1	0	0	0	1	1	0	1	1	27
For state d2	0	0	0	1	1	1	0	0	28
For state d3	0	0	0	1	1	1	0	1	29
	0	0	0	1	1	1	1	1	31
Packet not allowed	0	0	1	0	0	0	0	0	32
Unidentifiable packet	0	0	1	0	0	0	0	1	33
Call on one-way logical channel	0	0	1	0	0	0	1	0	34

Diagnostics	Bits								Decimal
	8	7	6	5	4	3	2	1	
Invalid packet type on a permanent virtual circuit	0	0	1	0	0	0	1	1	35
Packet on unassigned logical channel	0	0	1	0	0	1	0	0	36
REJECT not subscribed to	0	0	1	0	0	1	0	1	37
Packet too short	0	0	1	0	0	1	1	0	38
Packet too long	0	0	1	0	0	1	1	1	39
Invalid general format identifier	0	0	1	0	1	0	0	0	40
RESTART or registration packet with nonzero in bits 1 to 4 of octet 1, or bits 1 to 8 of octet 2	0	0	1	0	1	0	0	1	41
Packet type not compatible with facility	0	0	1	0	1	0	1	0	42
Unauthorized INTERRUPT CONFIRMATION	0	0	1	0	1	0	1	1	43
Unauthorized INTERRUPT	0	0	1	0	1	1	0	0	44
Unauthorized REJECT	0	0	1	0	1	1	0	1	45
	0	0	1	0	1	1	1	1	47
Time expired	0	0	1	1	0	0	0	0	48
For INCOMING CALL	0	0	1	1	0	0	0	1	49
For CLEAR INDICATION	0	0	1	1	0	0	1	0	50
For RESET INDICATION	0	0	1	1	0	0	1	1	51
For RESTART INDICATION	0	0	1	1	0	1	0	0	52
	0	0	1	1	1	1	1	1	63
Call set up, call clearing or registration problem	0	1	0	0	0	0	0	0	64
Facility/registration code not allowed	0	1	0	0	0	0	0	1	65
Facility parameter not allowed	0	1	0	0	0	0	1	0	66
Invalid called address	0	1	0	0	0	0	1	1	67
Invalid calling address	0	1	0	0	0	1	0	0	68
Invalid facility/registration length	0	1	0	0	0	1	0	1	69
Incoming call barred	0	1	0	0	0	1	1	0	70
No logical channel available	0	1	0	0	0	1	1	1	71
Call collision	0	1	0	0	1	0	0	0	72
Duplicate facility requested	0	1	0	0	1	0	0	1	73
Nonzero address length	0	1	0	0	1	0	1	0	74
Nonzero facility length	0	1	0	0	1	0	1	1	75
Facility not provided when expected	0	1	0	0	1	1	0	0	76
Invalid CCITT-specified DTE facility	0	1	0	0	1	1	0	1	77
	0	1	0	0	1	1	1	1	79
Miscellaneous	0	1	0	1	0	0	0	0	80
Improper cause code from DTE	0	1	0	1	0	0	0	1	81

Diagnostics	Bits								Decimal
	8	7	6	5	4	3	2	1	
Not aligned octet	0	1	0	1	0	0	1	0	82
Inconsistent Q-bit setting	0	1	0	1	0	0	1	1	83
	0	1	0	1	1	1	1	1	95
Not assigned	0	1	1	0	0	0	0	0	96
	0	1	1	0	1	1	1	1	111
International problem	0	1	1	1	0	0	0	0	112
Remote network problem	0	1	1	1	0	0	0	1	113
International protocol problem	0	1	1	1	0	0	1	0	114
International link out of order	0	1	1	1	0	0	1	1	115
International link busy	0	1	1	1	0	1	0	0	116
Transit network faciity problem	0	1	1	1	0	1	0	1	117
Remote network faciity problem	0	1	1	1	0	1	1	0	118
International routeing problem	0	1	1	1	0	1	1	1	119
Temporary routeing problem	0	1	1	1	1	0	0	0	120
Unknown called DNIC	0	1	1	1	1	0	0	1	121
Maintenance action	0	1	1	1	1	0	1	0	122
	0	1	1	1	1	1	1	1	127
Reserved for network specific diagnostic information	1	0	0	0	0	0	0	0	128
	1	1	1	1	1	1	1	1	255

Source: CCITT Recommendation X.25, 1984.

Appendix C

Logical channel assignment

Logical channels may be divided into four catetories (Figure C.1):

1. Permanent virtual circuits. No call set-up will be required as the LCN is permanently in the data transfer state.

2. One-way incoming calls. Calls may only be initiated by the DCE (Exchange) with an INCOMING CALL packet. If all logical channels are assigned to one way, this will have the same effect as the outgoing calls barred facility.

3. Two-way switched calls. Unrestricted switched virtual circuits that may have incoming and outgoing calls.

4. One-way outgoing calls. In this case only the DTE (Terminal) may initiate calls by using the CALL REQUEST packet. If all LCNs are designated as outgoing only, this will have the same effect as the incoming calls barred facility.

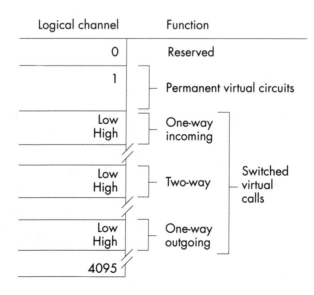

Figure C.1 Logical channel assignment.

Glossary

ABM: Asynchronous Balanced Mode –
allows two-way communication.

ACK: Acknowledgement – a character
transmitted by a receiver to indicate
that a message was received correctly.

ADDRESS: A coded representation of the
destination of a message.

ANSI: American National Standards
Institute.

ARPA: American Research Projects
Agency.

ASCII: American Standard Code for
Information Interchange.

ASYNCHRONOUS: A method of
communication by which individual
character representations are bounded
by a start and stop bit.

BANDWIDTH: A measurement of the
signalling space available on a
communications channel.

BAUD (baud rate): An expression that is
loosely used in data communications.
It strictly refers to modulation rate.

BCD: Binary Coded Decimal – a coding
scheme used to represent individual
decimal characters.

BIT: A BInary digiT.

BIT RATE (bps, bits per second): The rate
at which bits are transmitted over a
communications channel.

BNA: Burrough's Network Architecture –
a structured layered network.

BSC: Bisync – a data link control
procedure developed by IBM using
character synchronization.

BT: British Telecom (the UK's PTT).

BYTE: A unit consisting of a sequence of
eight bits.

CCITT: The International Telegraph and
Telephone Consultative Committee.

CHARACTER TERMINAL: Sometimes
referred to as a 'dumb terminal', it will
send and receive data on a character by
character basis (requires the use of a
PAD to communicate on a packet
network).

CRC: Cyclic Redundancy Check – a
method of detecting errors in a block of
data.

CUG: Closed User Group – allows a
nominated group of DTEs (Terminals)
to have privacy by not receiving/
sending unwanted calls from/to DTEs
(Terminals) outside the group.

DCE: Data Circuit Terminating
Equipment.

DIAL-UP: A method of connection that
allows a user to gain access to a
network using a modem and a
conventional telephone line.

DIFFERENTIAL: A signal that is used in
two forms consisting of an 'in-phase'
signal and an 'opposite-phase' signal –
intended to overcome the problems of
'noise'

DM: Disconnect mode.

DNIC: Data Network Identification Code.

DTE: Data Terminal Equipment.

ECMA: European Computer
Manufacturer's Association.

EIA: Electronic Industries Association.

FAX: Facsimile machine.

FCS: Frame Check Sequence – a number
(usually a CRC) that enables the
integrity of received data to be verified.

FRAME: In a bit-oriented protocol, data

are formatted in frames along with other data for transmission.

FULL-DUPLEX: The ability of a communications system to transmit and receive data simultaneously.

GFI: General Format Identifier.

HALF-DUPLEX: Refers to a method whereby the system can only communicate in *one* direction at a time.

HDLC: High level Data Link Control – a link level, bit-oriented protocol (level 2 X.25).

IA5: International Alphabet No. 5 – a recognized character set.

IEEE: Institute of Electrical and Electronic Engineers.

IPSS: International Packet SwitchStream (British Telecom's international packet-switched service).

ISO: International Standards Organization.

kbps: Kilo bits per second (kilo = 1000).

Kilostream: A digital network that operates in the United Kingdom (typically 64 k).

LAP: Link Access Procedure.

LAPB: Link Access Procedure, Balanced.

LCGN: Logical Channel Group Number.

LCN: Logical Channel Number.

LEASED LINE: A dedicated communication path normally provided by the local telephone company. The user has to define where both ends of the connection is to be terminated. The connection could be 2-wire or 4-wire (a reference to the number of conductors presented to the user). The service is graded depending on quality required, i.e. amplified or non-amplified.

LINK: A transmission path between two communicating stations.

LSB: Least Significant Bit.

MARK: Represents a binary 1 and is usually negative (see SPACE).

Mbps: Mega bits per second. Mega = 1 000 000.

MEGASTREAM: A digital service that operates in the UK.

MINICALL: A term used to describe the Fast Select facility.

MNEMONIC: A coded representation of an address, operation or term, e.g. ADD = Address.

MODEM: Stands for MOdulator/ DEModulator. It is a device used to convert digital signals into an analogue signal for transmission on a network (usually voice grade or better).

ms: millisecond, 1000th of a second.

MSB: Most Significant Bit.

MULTIPLEXER: A device for combining several signals into one signal.

MULTIPOINT: To allow in one direction the transmission of signals from a central station to a number of outstations.

NETWORK: A series of points interconnected by communications links.

NODE: A point on a network where communications links join to link up with other nodes or users.

NTU: Network Termination Unit.

NUA: Network User Address.

NUI: Network User Identifier.

OCTET: A group of eight consecutive bits of user data.

OSI: Open Systems Interconnect – standardized procedures for the exchange of information among technical devices.

PACKET: Data grouped for transmission through a network, e.g. X.25.

PACKET SWITCHING: The transfer of data by means of addressed packets through a network.

PACKET TERMINAL: A terminal that can form packets for inter-working with a packet network.

PAD: Packet Assembler/Disassembler – required by devices that cannot form packets, i.e. a character terminal.

PARITY: A 'bit' added to characters so that the total of bits in a group will always be either even (even parity) or odd (odd parity).

POINT TO POINT: A single communication path between two stations.

PSS: British Telecom's Packet SwitchStream service.

PSTN: Public Switched Telephone
Network.
PTT: Public Telegraph and Telephone
Administration.
PUBLIC DATA NETWORK (PDN): A
network provided for the general
public.
PVC: Permanent Virtual Circuit.
REJ: REJECT.
RPOA: Recognized Private Operating
Agency.
RNR: RECEIVER NOT READY.
RR: RECEIVER READY.
SABM: Set Asynchronous Balanced
Mode.
SDLC: Synchronous Data Link Control –
a protocol.
SNA: Systems Network Architecture – an
IBM-structured communications
system.

SPACE: Represents a binary 'zero' and is
usually positive.
SVC: Switched Virtual Circuit.
SWITCHED NETWORK: A path through
a network is only built during the call
establishment phase, and cleared down
after the call is terminated. For
example, telephone networks usually
operate in this manner.
SYNCHRONOUS: Refers to a method of
communication used by packet
terminals.
TERMINAL: A device by which the user
is able to gain access to the service
required, i.e. a network.
V-SERIES: A series of voice-grade CCITT
interface and modem specifications.
X-SERIES: A series of CCITT
recommendations for transmission of
data over 'public data networks'.

Index